THE MAN IN POSSESSION

by

HILDA PRESSLEY

Harlequin Books

TORONTO • LONDON • NEW YORK • AMSTERDAM • SYDNEY • WINNIPEG

Sheryl Henley

Original hardcover edition published in 1969
by Mills & Boon Limited

ISBN 0-373-01429-5

Harlequin edition published September 1970
Reprinted 1976

Printed in Canada

CHAPTER ONE

The auction room was crowded. Julia Barclay glanced around at the faces of the prospective buyers. By sight and by reputation she knew quite a number of them very well indeed; for the most part they were property owners and property developers, land owners and the owners of hire-fleet. There were some very interesting properties to be auctioned this morning, all of them situated in and around the Broads area for which Norfolk was famed.

But Julia was interested in one item only. Wingcraft, the name of the boatyard and its fleet of hire craft owned by her late employers, the man who had almost been her father-in-law.

'I can see Windbush's men,' and someone from Jenkins',' said the man at her side.

'Yes.' Julia had seen them too, but now, her eye caught that of a tall stranger across the room. He was standing beside a window apparently doing the same thing as herself—assessing the opposition. He had thick dark hair and was hatless, his sheepskin coat open, one hand in his pocket, the other holding his catalogue. She wondered fleetingly who he was, and thought from the set of his jaw that he would be the kind of man who usually got what he wanted.

'I told Father's man not to bid against you, of course.'

Julia brought her gaze slowly to the man sitting next to her. Max Windham's father had taken over several small boatyards in the area. Normally, he would very likely have wanted this one, too.

'Thank you, Max,' she said, giving him a smile. 'That's very good of you. Did your father say whether or not he wanted it?'

Max shrugged. 'Well, we did discuss it, but he said

5

he'd leave it with me.'

'In that case, thanks again.'

He put his hand on her shoulder, his features softening as his eyes dwelt on her face.

'You know I'd do anything for you any time,' he said softly.

She shifted her gaze from his swiftly. Max frequently said things like that, and she was grateful for his friendship, but somehow, since David's death—even though it was well over a year ago—she couldn't feel anything for another man beyond ordinary liking. She supposed that by working for David's father she had kept his memory more acutely alive. But he was more than merely a memory to her. She had learned to do his job in his father's boatyard, walking where he had walked, sitting in the chair he had occupied, sailing the boat which had once belonged to him. She had seemed to hear his voice a dozen times a day. Now his father was dead too, and she was determined to buy Wingcraft if at all possible.

'Pity Hargreaves never made a will,' murmured Max.

Julia smiled. 'In my favour, you mean?'

'Why not? You've done more for him than that sister of his in Australia.'

But Julia shook her head. 'He paid me a good enough salary. I don't suppose he thought about dying, anyway. It happened so suddenly. But if only his sister had been willing to take my offer!'

'I expect she thought she could get more money if it were auctioned. But it could turn out the other way unless she's put a considerable reserve price on it,' Max said.

Julia prayed that not too high a reserve had been put on the boatyard. She simply could not bear the idea of the place passing into someone else's hands. She almost felt it belonged to her. John Hargreaves had come to rely on her more and more. She had practically run the place during the last few months. He had cared

6

only about the boatbuilding part of the business. Then one morning he had crossed the road to the Broadland store, apparently without looking where he was going, and had been knocked down by a bus.

The auction was starting. Julia's muscles tensed nervously. Her parents had given her a few hundred pounds as a present when she had become engaged, then six months ago an endownment policy her mother had taken out for her when she was a child had become due. This, added to some savings, had afforded a down payment on a mortgage a solicitor was willing to arrange for her to buy the boatyard property. The house adjacent in which David and his father had lived was being sold separately. This was one thing about which Julia was thankful. She could never have afforded to buy both.

The first item to be auctioned was a riverside hotel. The bidding started at a very high price. Julia's glance strayed in the direction of the tall stranger. This might be his kind of property. Or would it be the second item—the Georgian house overlooking one of the Broads with a hundred and twenty feet of water frontage and thirty acres of land? He looked affluent enough. He had that bearing of confidence and authority which often accompanied money and position, and the tweed suit showing beneath his sheepskin jacket looked expensive.

As if aware of her scrutiny he turned and looked straight at her. With a feeling of embarrassment she withdrew her gaze swiftly and turned her attention on the auctioneer.

The stranger did not bid for either the first item or the second, however. He opened the bidding for Wingcraft.

'Oh, *no*—!' she breathed, quickly making her own bid.

'Why, do you know him?' asked Max.

'No, but he looks as though money might be no object if he really wants anything,' she answered, raising her catalogue as the auctioneer glanced her way.

Two other boatowners, who own a string of boatyards, were also bidding, but Julia knew that they had a price beyond which they would not go, and she had been prepared to carry on when they had stopped.

Very soon the only two people bidding were the stranger and herself. Julia's limit was reached and passed.

' Go on, Julia, carry on,' Max urged her. ' I can let you have a hundred or so.'

She hesitated. She did not *want* to put herself under an obligation to Max.

' Are there any more bids?' came the auctioneer's cultured voice, glancing in Julia's direction. ' Going— going at—'

In desperation Julia added another hundred. Perhaps her father would lend her some more.

But whoever he was, the stranger seemed willing to go on bidding indefinitely. Julia made another bid. He raised it. Urged on by Max, Julia made two more, this time adding only fifty pounds. But this only protracted the business.

' It's no *use*—' she murmured desperately. ' He means to have it.'

' Everybody has their limit, Julia, don't let him beat you.'

Max put his hand under her elbow and raised her arm. Her catalogue caught the auctioneer's eye just before his hammer came down. The atmosphere in the room was now tense. The stranger glanced across the room as once more Max pushed up her hand holding the catalogue. But Julia knew it was hopeless.

' No, Max, I mustn't bid any more. I can't. I'm five hundred over my limit, as it is. I'd be ruined before I started.'

The next time the auctioneer glanced her way she shook her head and a babble of conversation broke out as his hammer came down.

'That's a fantastic price,' Max declared. 'Nobody who knows anything at all about the business would have paid it. I only urged you on because I know how much it meant to you.'

Julia lowered her head, overwhelmed with disappointment. The boatyard had become her life. Suppose the new owner did not approve of a woman managing his business, if only the office side? Or even of having a woman working for him at all? Besides, she did not *want* to work for someone else.

'I must go,' she said suddenly to Max. 'But don't you bother—'

Max half rose. 'But don't you want to wait and see whether he buys the house, too?'

She shook her head swiftly. All she wanted to do was get out into the fresh air, to go somewhere to think.

'You stay, and—let me know what happens,' she said.

'Yes, sure. See you later, then.'

He subsided into his seat, and Julia made her way out, conscious of both curious and sympathetic looks. Her whole body seeming to ache with disappointment. Her throat and eyes heavy with gathering tears, she crossed the road to the car park. She had no car of her own now. She had sold it towards the deposit she hoped to have required for the mortgage on the boatyard, thinking that the firm's small van would serve her needs well enough.

She drove back to the boatyard along mushy, sand-coloured roads lined with February snow, the whole of the countryside under a four-inch blanket. It was like this in Kent too, according to the television, and a letter she had received from her mother that morning. Her father owned extensive apple orchards there, and until she had come to Norfolk to be with David she had helped him with the management of them.

It was about this time of the year she had met David. It was just about the only time he could really be spared

9

away from the boatyard, and he had been visiting friends one week-end in the small Kentish town where her parents lived. They had fallen in love at first sight. Letters had followed, then an invitation to visit Norfolk in the early spring. It was during the visit they realised that they had fallen headlong in love. There had been a strange urgency about their love, as if they had known that in a few brief weeks' time they would be parted for ever. Julia's visit had extended into weeks, made possible by understanding parents. Then three days before the date they had fixed for their wedding, David had been killed in a road accident. He had been everything to his father, whose wife had died when the boy was fourteen. He was their first and only child, and John Hargreaves had never married again. In comforting him and helping him in the boatyard office, Julia found solace for her own grief.

Soon she became indispensable to him. He could not bear the thought of another man taking his son's place, and Julia could not bear to leave the surroundings in which she had known such wonderful happiness, brief as it had been. She seemed to be held here by invisible bonds created by the love she and David had had for each other. She simply could not go.

But what now? she asked herself, as she turned down the narrow lane leading to the boatyard. Now that she had failed in her attempt to buy the business would she feel a slackening of the bonds which had held her? What plans would the new owner have? She imagined the man she had seen in the auction room would not be very easy to please. And again the thought came that he might object to having a woman about the place at all. It occurred to her suddenly that he was probably married and that his wife might possibly want to help him in the business. Though it could be hectic in the height of the holiday season, it could be very pleasant indeed in warm sunny weather helping to bring in the craft to moor, giving a helping hand to a novice to hoist a sail, taking one of the cruiser hirers for a trial run up the river, or just to stand and stare, watching a swan in flight, the wind rippling the surface of the water or a family of brown ducks paddling one behind the other.

But at present a film of ice encrusted the small docks, and the boats which normally moored there when not out on hire were safely in the shelter of the large boat-house or repair shed—craft all with the word Wing forming part of the name. Yachts called Redwing, and Lapwing, Blue Wing, Grey Wing, Light Wing and Swallow's Wing. The cruisers, Wing of Happiness, Wing of Delight, Wing of Joy and Wing of the Morning. And when David and his father could not think of other names, numbers were added.

Julia left the car and went in search of Frank Willis, the maintenance foreman. He and the workmen would all be anxious to know what had happened.

The boathouse was a warm, untidy—at least to the uninitiated—friendly place, all the general paraphernalia of boat maintenance scattered around. Pots of paint and varnish, oars, masts, coils of rope, pulley blocks, rowlocks, anchors of various kinds, and in the centre a large black stove aglow with heat on which a large brown kettle steamed invitingly. Nearby, an ex-houseboat table, cluttered with mugs and beakers, a teapot, a bottle of milk and a packet of tea half used. Julia picked her way carefully among the general clutter and went to where the men were working. As she approached they glanced up swiftly.

' Any luck, miss?' asked the foreman anxiously.

Julia shook her head slowly. ' I'm afraid not, Frank. I had to drop out. The price was much too high. I did my best, but—'

' Strewth! Well, that's a turn-up for the book. Who in blazes was it?'

' A stranger—at any rate, to me,' she told him gloomily.

' What'd 'e look loike, miss?' asked Andy, the

youngest of the workmen. 'I mean, is 'e young or old or—what?'

Julia sighed. 'Neither, really. Thirtyish, I'd say. Tall, well dressed—'

'You mean—collar an' tie an' all that?'

She smiled. 'Yes, but country clothes.'

Andy gave a desisive grunt. 'An office wallah, I expect. Somebody who knows nothing at all about boats or engines, somebody what'll sit in the office all day, then come out 'ere expectin' we've performed miracles.'

'We'll just have to wait and see, won't we, Andy?' Julia said, thinking privately that the boy could well be right.

'What will you do, miss?' asked Frank Willis.

'That I don't know, Frank. I'll have to think about it.'

'Did he buy the house as well?' he asked, as she turned to go.

'I didn't wait to find out,' she told him over her shoulder.

The house had been for sale as it stood—furniture and all. Julia could not remember anyone coming to view the place. As David and his father had had no resident housekeeper, just a daily woman, Mr Hargreaves had offered Julia the use of one of the houseboats when David had died. It was as warm and comfortable as a house. Main electricity and water were connected so that she could use an electric cooker and have a fire in each compartment—bedroom, sitting-room and galley. The walls and ceiling were insulated and she had thick-pile carpeting throughout. She had even a tiny bathroom and a small refrigerator.

Her using the houseboat as living quarters meant that it could not be let out on hire, naturally, and Mr Hargreaves had refused to accept any rent from her. The fact that he had probably been losing anything from two to three hundred pounds a year had not appeared to worry him in the least. But it might worry the new owner. How soon could she expect him to visit his property? This afternoon?

She cooked a light lunch for herself, then went across to the office. There was little else she could do for the time being except carry on with her work and await developments. There were one or two letters to be answered, then she would continue with her job of going through the linen, examining for repair or replacement, the sheets, pillow cases, tablecloths, tea-towels and blankets which would be used on the hire-craft during the rapidly approaching season. The popularity of a Broads holiday increased year by year, bookings beginning earlier and finishing later. Last year they had had some as late as November—a houseboat letting even for Christmas—and bookings this year began in March.

Julia dealt with the correspondence, glancing at the door somewhat apprehensively every time she heard footsteps outside, thinking it might be the new owner. She couldn't understand why she had not seen him before. Surely he had been to look over the boatyard before deciding to make a bid for either that or the house? He could have come while she had been in Wroxham or Norwich in search of supplies or something the workmen were waiting for, but none of them had seen anyone looking around, either, otherwise they would have said so. Living in the houseboat, she herself would have been here even on Sundays. But perhaps the man had been content with a list and description of the boats, sheds, wet docks, land area and chattels.

She posted the letters, made some necessary telephone calls, then went into the linen store. How many more times would she do this? she wondered. Did she really want to stay on, working for a stranger, someone who might have totally different ideas of running things? She had planned to make one or two changes herself, if she had been successful in buying the boatyard. She would like to have more sailing dinghies available for day hire, more two, three and four-berth yachts for holiday hire. There were far too many large cruisers on the Broads, Julia felt, their number ever-increasing, and too few sailing craft. The climate was mainly responsible, of course. A week of rain and squalls spent either getting wet through in the open well of a yacht or being forced to sit in the cabin was not ideal, to put it mildly. But Julia maintained that the design of some yachts was at fault. Naturally a vessel meant purely for sailing, with no power at all beyond the sails, was impossible to navigate under cover. The boom needed to swing free, the main sheet—the nautical term for the main rope which controlled the mainsail—needed space and access and the yachtsman often had to move about swiftly. This was the holiday for the dedicated yachtsman, the young and the tough, those who did not mind 'roughing it,' if necessary.

But for the auxiliary, or cruiser-yachts—those with an inboard engine as well as sail—Julia would like to see an entirely new design, so that when under power, with the sails furled, the holiday-maker could go along under cover. At present, when the well cover of a yacht was *in situ* it was impossible for the yachtsman to see where he was going. The term cruiser-yacht was a misnomer. Their crews still had to navigate out in the open—wonderful in fine weather, of course—while the cruisers proper had efficient awnings with windscreens, and hirers could be on the move in either fair weather or foul.

If she had been able to buy the business she would have set about designing one, had an expert to draw the plan for her and put Frank Willis to work on building it. He could do it. He was a boat-builder, not merely a maintenance man. He had helped David and his father to build the whole of the existing Wing fleet.

Another thing she would have done, her thoughts went on as she tried to decide whether or not a sheet would stand another season without some holiday-maker putting his foot through it, was gradually to replace these white cotton sheets with fitted nylon. Pillow cases, too. What a saving on laundry bills, and even her present task would be unnecesary.

'Hello there. Deep in thought?'

She swung round to see Max. 'Oh, hello—I didn't hear you come in.'

He sat on a pile of mattresses and grinned up at her. 'That was obvious. I suppose you weren't by any possible, improbable chance thinking about me?'

She shook her head. 'Sorry. Something much more —mundane. About replacing these outdated things with nylon.

He screwed up his face. 'My dear girl, you must be mad! Think of the initial cost. They'd have to be specially made to fit the bunks. And you couldn't just order one pair at a time, or any of that lark. You'd have to replace the whole lot at once. Most impractical.'

'Never heard of bulk buying?' But she sighed. 'The new man would no doubt agree with you.' There was a pause. 'Did he—buy the house?'

'He did—and at a give-away price. So what he lost on the roundabouts, he gained on the swings, so to speak.'

'He intends living here, then,' she said gloomily.

'Looks like it. Were you hoping he'd leave you to it?'

'To manage the business? I'm not sure what I was hoping. I suppose it *was* in the back of my mind that he might possibly get a manager or something. I don't suppose for a moment he'd let *me* run it, even if he didn't want to manage the business himself. But what's the good of talking? It looks as though he intends living here, and where I shall come in or what I shall do

15

'I simply don't know. By the way, I wonder what his name is?'

'Leighton,' Max said promptly. 'R. Leighton. I found out that much from the clerk. In fact, I've been finding out quite a few things about friend Leighton.'

'What sort of things?' she asked, wondering vaguely what the initial stood for. Robert? Ralph—or Richard, perhaps?

'Well, one thing's for sure,' said Max. 'He can't be short of money. In fact, I should think he's pretty well loaded.'

'That was the impression I got. But what makes you say so, apart from the price he paid for Wingcraft?'

Max sprawled out full length on the mattresses, his hands behind his head.

'Because, my love, he's the only son of the managing director of the Melloid oil company, no less. Moreover, he was a director of the company himself—and those fellows get fabulous salaries, not to mention perks.'

Julia frowned. 'Yes, I suppose they do. But if he has a job like that what on earth does he want with a boat-hire business?'

'As I see it, there are two possible—and probable— theories. One, he's had a row with his father and has packed it in. Fathers can be regular cusses to work for, as I know only too well. Two, buying this business is just a whim—the kind that the rich do sometimes get. He'll maybe hire a manager—people like him are more used to having women in the role of private secretaries than managers, and in any case, you couldn't manage things without help. He'll maybe hire a manager, keep you on for the office work, and just come down here for week-ends and holidays. How would that be?'

Julia pulled a face and switched on the light against the gathering gloom of the place. She wasn't sure she wanted to be 'kept on for the office work'.

'You could be right,' she told Max. 'On the other hand, you could be entirely wrong. The only thing to do is wait and see. I don't really know what I shall do yet. Probably go back home. Father can always use help in the orchards.'

Max sat up. ' Go back home—to Kent?' he echoed in consternation. ' You can't do that. It's unthinkable. Oh, Julia, you wouldn't be so cru-el!'

She reached to a top shelf for the last pile of pillow cases. ' You'll survive,' she told him mildly.

' I shan't, you know.'

Max stretched out his hand and pulled her towards him so suddenly, she lost her balance and sat down heavily beside him on the mattress, scattering the pillow cases in all directions.

' Max, what on earth—'

' I'll show you whether I'll survive or not,' he said, putting his arms about her and trying to kiss her.

She pushed against him and they toppled over backwards on to the mattresses. He held her fast and his lips found hers. She tried to free her arms, then suddenly the door opened. Max let her go and she sat up breathless, angry, and dishevelled, to see the new owner of Wingcraft standing there.

He stared at them in astonishment. ' May I ask who you are—and why you are using my property for your own private—use?'

Julia was on her feet, her face taut with anger and mingled humiliation. Max ran his fingers through his hair, and there was a smile of amusement on his face.

' I just came to see Julia, that's all, and we—er—got carried away. Who wouldn't? But I'll be off. Be seeing you, Julia,' and with a mocking salute he walked out.

Julia took a deep breath. ' I'm—sorry about that, Mr—'

' My name's Leighton. Didn't I see you in the auction room this morning? Your boy-friend too?'

' He's not my boy-friend,' she retorted emphatically.

17

'No? That makes your conduct even worse.'

'He's a *friend*, Mr Leighton,' she said evenly. 'A far different thing from what I imagine you have in mind.'

'Really?' he said coldly. His glance flicked to the pillow cases scattered on the floor. 'Do I take it you work here?'

'Yes. I was going through the last few items of linen.' She bent to retrieve the pillow cases.

He waited until she straightened up again, then asked: 'As a matter of interest, why did you push up the bidding this morning?'

'I was bidding because I wanted to buy the business,' she told him brusquely.

'*You* wanted to buy it?' he asked incredulously. 'But why?'

'Why not?' she countered.

He gave her a puzzled look. 'It's hardly a woman's line of business, surely? Though I suppose there are things a woman can do. Office work, attending to the linen. I take it there's a manager?'

'There is not. Mr Hargreaves only died a few weeks ago. I've been looking after things.'

'Oh, I see,' he said slowly as though he thought that explained quite a lot.

'We have a maintenance and boatyard foreman, of course,' she told him. 'Would you like me to take you to see him or shall I find him for you and—'

'No, I can go and find him myself and see what the workmen are doing. How much more of this linen have you to do?'

'I've nearly finished, actually. Just these few,' she said, indicating the pillow cases.

'And there's no urgent office work?'

'Not really, but—'

'In that case, you can go home as soon as the linen is finished. There's no point in waiting until it's nearly dark, the state the roads are in. I'll see you in the office in the morning. At nine-thirty, sharp.'

Her jaw tightened. Already he was speaking to her as if she were nothing more than an office girl.

'I'm usually in the office by nine o'clock, Mr Leighton,' she answered stiffly. 'The post comes about that time in the winter, earlier in the summer, of course. And I've been in the habit of locking up the office at night so that I could get in in the mornings. However—'

She broke off, sending the ball into his court, then waited to see what his answer would be.

He gave her a cool glance. 'Some of your habits might have to be broken, Miss— By the way, what *is* your name, apart from Julia?'

'Barclay,' she supplied, inwardly fuming.

'Miss Barclay,' he continued. 'I will lock the office tonight and I shall be glad if you will report to me in the morning at the time I have already mentioned. If you arrive earlier than that, you can occupy yourself elsewhere.'

He went out, closing the door behind him with a decisive little slam. Julia compressed her lips furiously. Obviously he was going to be impossible to work for. Simply impossible. She finished her job swiftly and took her coat from the hook behind the door. She crossed over to her houseboat, wishing with all her heart that spring was here. At times like these when she felt depressed or had a problem, she would take one of the dinghies out and go for a row or, if there was enough breeze, push off in one of the half-deckers for a sail. There was simply nothing like a spell on the river for soothing away small irritations, reducing others to manageable proportions and giving one the strength to endure what could not be cured. But the river was frozen solid enough for skating, and skating was something she had not learned to do.

The outside bell of the telephone rang noisily and automatically she crossed to the office to answer it. There was no sign of Mr Leighton and she presumed he had found Frank and the boys in the boathouse and repair shed. But as she opened the office door the telephone stopped ringing. Her new employer was answering it.

She murmured an apology and went out again, but she had not gone more than a couple of steps when the door opened again and he called after her.

'It's for you,' he said. 'A personal call, I presume. Will you make it clear to that young man that you *work* here?'

Not any longer than I can help, she called out silently after his retreating back as he walked in the direction of the boathouse. It was only a small office, consisting merely of one room with a counter and one typist's desk. An inner room housed portable radio and television sets, and did duty as an odds and ends room, but there was no office furniture in there.

She lifted the receiver to find it was Max at the other end.

'Hullo, Julia. How goes it?' he asked.

'Not too good—thanks in no small measure to you,' she answered, still angry with him because of what he did in the storeroom.

'I'm sorry about that. Really I am.'

'So you ought to be.'

'Well, how was I to know he was going to walk in at precisely that moment?'

'That's not the point,' she told him. 'What gave you the idea you could do what you did, anyhow?'

'Oh, come off it, Julia. We're not strangers, and surely I'm not all that repulsive? Let me take you out to dinner tonight to make up. I promise I won't try to rough-house you again.'

But Julia did not feel in the mood for being wined and dined.

'Not tonight, Max, if you don't mind. I want to think things out.'

'What sort of things?' he queried. 'You weren't

20

really serious about going back home?'

'I might go for a little while, anyway. One thing I *am* sure about. Nothing would induce me to work for this man. Just nothing!'

CHAPTER TWO

It cost Julia a great deal to write out her notice and place it before her new boss the following morning. She did not want to leave here. David, and the place where he had once lived and worked, meant a great deal to her. She loved the work, she loved the county and liked its people. But she simply could not see Mr Leighton and herself working amicably together. Indeed, she felt working *together* would not be the relationship he would have in mind. He had left her in no doubt whatever that he was the boss. This she could have accepted, even though she had wanted to manage the business herself, but she did not want a job where she had no responsibility and could never act on her own initiative. Moreover, she had a strong suspicion that *she* was going to be given notice, so she had forestalled him. But she felt far from happy and she couldn't help feeling that there were difficult days ahead in either case.

He looked up at her keenly as he picked up the envelope she had placed before him. He opened it and barely glanced at its contents.

'Sit down, Miss Barclay, and let's talk,' he said in the courteous, half friendly, half businesslike tone a managing director might use towards one of his senior staff.

Julia hesitated, but as she would have to work out her notice in any case, she supposed some talk was necessary. She sat down. He offered her a cigarette, but she declined.

'I don't, thanks, except on very odd occasions, and I prefer not to at this hour.'

He put the case back in his pocket, and she noticed that he did not light one for himself. He sat back in his chair looking relaxed, yet entirely in command.

Julia eyed him warily and guarded herself against his

undoubted masculine attractiveness. She could well imagine the beautiful, efficient, impeccably and fashionabily dressed private secretary pandering to his every whim and dancing attendance upon him; the little typists scurrying around, half worshipping him, half afraid of him. By some means or another this man would bend everyone's will to suit his own. But she determined he was not going to bend hers. If she changed her mind about staying on, it would be because she wanted to herself.

'How long have you been working for this firm, Miss Barclay?' was his first question.

'About nine months.'

He nodded, as though she had merely confirmed what he already knew. 'I spent some time last night going through the files and the account books. This office has been very efficiently run for just about that time, from the look of the dates on some of the copies of letters. This, I take it, is your work.'

'I did a great deal more than just office work, Mr Leighton,' she answered.

'So I believe. John Hargreaves had a son who used to manage the business. You more or less took over when the son died. A road accident, I understand.'

Julia kept her face impassive. 'That's right. I was on holiday here at the time. I stayed for a while to help out, then became—interested.'

His expression altered. 'Interested enough to want to own it? Or were you, in fact, bidding for someone else?'

She gave him an icy look. 'I told you last night that I wanted to buy it. I'm not used to having my word doubted. I consider lying to be both cowardly and undignified. Perhaps you would like a month's salary from me in lieu of notice? I have no wish to work a single day longer for someone who can't trust me nor tell when a person is telling the truth.'

She rose to her feet. He eyed her calmly, then stood

up himself and indicated the chair.

'I apologise. Do sit down again. I had to be sure, you see. It seemed to me from where I was standing in the auction room that your friend was urging you on to raise the bidding, and when I found out later that he was the son of a boat-owner who had taken over several other firms, I thought—'

'You're right in a way. But he was urging me to keep bidding because he knew how much I'd set my heart on having the business. I would have stopped long before I did, having reached my ceiling price.'

'Then why did you go on?'

'For the very simple reason that he offered to lend me the extra money. But I knew I would have to pay him back, so—'

'You've no intention of marrying him, then?'

She looked puzzled. 'Why do you ask?'

But it was evident that he wanted to ask all the questions and was not prepared to answer any. He brushed her query aside.

'It doesn't matter. I—take it his attentions were—unwelcome yesterday evening?'

Her chin lifted. 'That incident was totally unexpected *and* unusual, I can assure you. Such a thing isn't likely to happen again.'

'I'm glad to hear it. Now. Having cleared up a few preliminary matters, perhaps we can get down to business. I never believe in breaking up a good working team. Frank Willis seems to know what he's doing with regard to maintenance and general boatbuilding, and you certainly have the office work and stores at your finger-tips. The workmen are willing to carry on. I spoke to them last night. Now, I'm asking *you* if you'll carry on as before.'

Julia eyed him uncertainly. 'You mean you're—not going to be here most of the time?'

His eyes widened. 'Oh, I'm going to be here all right. What made you think otherwise?'

She shrugged. ' I simply thought you might regard a business like this as a sort of sideline and be here only at week-ends and during holiday periods.'

' Oh, no,' he said emphatically. ' That's not the way I do things at all. I mean to settle down here, believe me, and I mean to make a success of this business.'

Julia felt some very definite misgivings. Would he try to bring the methods of big business into the boat-yard? Streamline everything and expect the men to account for every screw or fathom of rope?

' I'm sure you will, Mr Leighton,' she answered stiffly. ' Though this is already quite a paying business.'

' I daresay. But tell me honestly, Miss Barclay. If you had been successful in buying the boatyard, wouldn't you have made some changes—changes that you couldn't very well have made before? In the past you might have taken quite a bit of responsibility—efficient people generally have plenty thrust upon them, too much sometimes—but Mr Hargreaves made the major decisions, I'm sure.'

' Of course.'

He nodded. ' And so will I, naturally. But you must have made some plans—had some changes in mind, and surely agree that there's room for improvement?'

' In some respects, yes. But what had *you* in mind, Mr Leighton?'

' This office, to begin with,' he said, indicating the shabby counter, the hardboard, colour-washed walls which needed redecorating, the worn lino on the floor and the old-fashioned electric fire.

Julia's lips twitched in sudden humour. ' I admit it's not exactly an executive suite.'

He gave her a sharp, enquiring glance. ' Why do you make that particular comparison, may I ask?'

She realised she had spoken without thinking, and that it would have been more diplomatic to have waited until he chose to tell her about himself. Nevertheless, she stood her ground.

'I've been finding out things, too. My particular grapevine tells me you're an—ex-director of Melloid Oil. Or have I been misinformed?'

A hard look came into his eyes, then he closed them momentarily as if recollections were also painful.

'No, you haven't been misinformed.' He picked up a pencil and began to doodle.

She waited for him to continue, but he appeared deep in thought. Then suddenly, as if emerging from a bad dream, he ripped off the sheet of paper from the pad and screwing it into a ball threw it into the waste-paper basket impatiently.

'Now where were we? Oh, yes, this office. You admit that something needs doing to it?'

'As a matter of fact, it was going to be my next job,' she told him.

He stared at her. '*Your* next job? What on earth do you mean by that? What were you going to do, for heaven's sake?'

She shrugged. 'Well, re-paint the walls for a start. Now that I've finished taking stock of the cabin equipment, I'll have some spare time in the afternoons. The mail doesn't take long at this time of the year, and—'

'You mean you'd actually buy a tin of paint and start working on the walls yourself? I never heard anything so ridiculous in all my life! The whole place wants knocking down and building afresh.'

'But—' She stopped suddenly.

Again, that direct look from the man's blue-grey eyes. 'Well? But what? Out with it.'

'I'm not sure that I should, Mr Leighton.'

'Oh, really!' he said on a note of exasperation. 'I've had enough of polite secretaries who only give an opinion when asked for. I thought you'd be more honest. That's why I—'

'You forget, Mr Leighton, I am *not* your private secretary. I haven't even said whether I'm prepared to go on working for you or not yet.'

26

'Haven't you? I thought you had. Well, for goodness' sake let's get it settled. Do you want to discuss salary? Whatever you're getting I feel sure it isn't enough.'

'It's not a question of money,' she told him.

'No? What then?'

She could hardly say she was not sure whether she wanted to work for him on personal grounds, though she was certainly going contrary to what she had said to Max over the telephone. Indeed, she was beginning to have quite a sneaking respect for the new owner of Wingcraft. His manner was direct and straightforward. She felt he was a man whose word one could always trust.

'If you don't mind, Mr Leighton,' she answered, 'I think I'd prefer to talk further, then go away and think the matter over for a little while.'

'Very well,' he said, looking a little surprised. 'Let's start again. We can discuss the question of salary later —that is, if you deside to stay on. And I hope you do. You were about to comment on the office.'

She inclined her head. 'If you insist. I was about to say that, in general, the building itself is quite adequate—and in keeping—for a boatyard office. The inside needs smartening up, that's all. If I were going to do it thoroughly, I'd also have a new counter. In fact, new furniture altogether and—' she gave an amused smile—'a new electric fire or something.'

'I should hope so. But wouldn't you have a carpet —on this side of the counter, at least?'

She shook her head. 'I don't think so. One is continually tramping in and out, and in wet weather—' she broke off, then went on, 'though some rush matting on this side might be a compromise, and I think now that you've come, it might be a good idea to have an inner office. We can find another place for the radio and television sets. I suppose that was what the other room was intended for originally. An office, I mean. But Mr Hargreaves spent most of his time in the repair

27

and boatbuilding sheds.'

'Point taken,' he said, and it was hard to tell whether he was smiling or not. 'But your idea's a good one. And I couldn't agree more about this office furniture. I'll attend to it myself. By the way, there seems to be one piece of essential equipment missing—which rather surprises me.'

'Yes?' she queried, wondering what on earth it could be. 'A computer, perhaps?' She couldn't resist the dig.

She could see by the look he gave her that her sarcasm had not been lost on him. He made no comment, however, and she began to think she would enjoy working with this man, after all.

'A kettle,' he told her. 'And all the wherewithal to make tea or coffee.'

'It somehow never seemed necessary, and at present there's only one power point. I'm afraid I often had a cup of tea with the workmen—I hope that doesn't offend your sense of propriety. And of course, my own place is quite near.'

Another look from him. She seemed to be continually surprising him. 'Oh yes, Frank Willis mentioned that you were living in one of the houseboats. I noticed your light on last night and asked him if it was let or something. I don't know that I like the idea.'

'For what reason?' she queried, hoping he was not going to object.

'Well, surely it's not very comfortable, especially in weather like this?'

She smiled and assured him that it was, and was on the point of explaining that her parents lived in Kent, otherwise she would not need the houseboat, but she stopped herself. That piece of information would almost inevitably bring the query: *Why did you come to Norfolk?* and she did not want to talk about David. In an effort to check any questions of that nature she asked one of her own.

28

'I take it you'll be living in the house, Mr Leighton?'

He nodded. 'I'm already in. I hate hotels. But that needs refurnishing and redecorating too. The décor is something awful.'

She felt a swift resentment on behalf of David and his father. Their furniture was not new. Some of it was old-fashioned and some of it was a little conventional, but it was good. Naturally most of the rooms needed redecorating, and man-like they had tended not to notice when things like carpets and curtains were looking shaby. But she put an end to these thoughts.

'May I ask if your wife is here with you yet?' she asked, with a view to offering to make him some coffee.

'That grapevine of yours isn't very good,' he answered. 'I'm a bachelor. Now is there anything else you'd like to know about me or that we have to settle immediately? If not—'

She stood up. 'I'm sorry. I didn't mean to—'

He rose too. 'For goodness' sake, don't feel obliged to keep apologizing. I can assure you, I shan't. There was one other thing. Quite important. If you do decide to stay on, and I'd like you to, you'd carry on pretty much as you did before, of course. As my assistant rather than my secretary. That suit you?'

'Why yes— In that case, I'll go through the mail. But I'll leave any important ones for you to see and sign, and if there are any queries—'

'Yes, yes,' he said briskly, going to the door.

'Mr Leighton—' she called out, ' I usually make coffee in the houseboat about eleven. Will you—join me?'

'Yes,' he said. 'Yes, all right.'

He shut the door behind him and she gazed at it half smiling, half puzzled. He was by no means an easy man, and she had a feeling there would often be a clash of wills between them, if she worked for him. But she was sure life would never be dull or boring.

She started on the mail and screwed up an envelope to drop it into the waste-paper basket. But her glance caught the sheet of crumpled paper on which he had been doodling. Suddenly curious, she took it out and smoothed it open. It was not so much a doodle as a very good drawing of a head.

The head of a very beautiful woman.

Julia stared at the drawing. This was someone he knew, she felt sure of it. Perhaps it wasn't a quarrel with his father which had led him to leave the firm. Perhaps it was a broken love affair. Men must suffer in that way just as women did. It was nonsense to suppose they didn't. And sometimes the only way to forget was to remove oneself from the scene which made it impossible or difficult. It was just the opposite with herself. She did not want memories of David to fade. They were far too precious to her.

She crumpled the doodle-drawing up again slowly and dropped it back into the waste-paper basket. She finished opening the mail and made some pencilled notes on each of them, then put on her sheepskin jacket and trudged through the snow to her houseboat.

Ten minutes later as the coffee was percolating she saw the shadow of Mr Leighton pass one of the windows.

'Smells wonderful,' he said, as she opened the door to him.

'Do you like it black or white?'

'Black, please,' he said, peeling off his tall rubber boots.

He looked round appreciatively as he entered the saloon with its studio couch, the cottage armchairs she had bought herself, the folding table and two dining chairs.

'This is different from the other houseboats,' he said. 'It hasn't a sun-deck or walk around verandah. I've just been having a look at some of them.'

'It is different,' she affirmed. 'This was actually designed for comfort—for winter bookings, in fact.'

'Winter bookings?' he echoed. 'Surely—'

'You'd be surprised. We've had bookings in November—even Christmas. It sleeps four. There's a two-berth cabin the other side of the galley, and of course the studio couch makes a double bed.'

' May I see around?' he asked.

' Of course.'

He slid past her to the sleeping cabin as she lifted the coffee from the cooker. She took cups and saucers into the saloon and set out cheese and biscuits.

' Who designed it?' he asked, coming into the saloon again and dropping on to the couch.

' Mr—Hargreaves' son,' she told him, pushing the table close to where he was sitting.

He eyed her intently. ' Did you know him?'

' Yes, I knew him. Sugar, Mr Leighton?'

He scooped up four spoonfuls of the Demerara sugar.

' And have some cheese and a biscuit,' she added.

She sat on one of the dining chairs and pulled it up to the table. It was odd, this feeling of not wanting to talk about David, especially as he still seemed so close to her. But somehow, his father and herself had never talked about him either. They had no need to. Each had known instinctively that David was never far from either of their thoughts. And now she supposed she wanted to keep David to herself.

' How long have you been living in here?' asked the new owner of Wingcraft.

' Oh, ever since—' she began without thinking, then broke off and ended: ' About seven or eight months.'

He gave her another of his looks and she feared he might ask her what she had been about to say when she broke off, but all he said was:

' You make very good coffee.'

She smiled. ' These things are very much a matter of individual taste. I'm glad I made it as you like it.'

He regarded her for a moment or two in silence, then asked: ' Have you made up your mind yet about staying on?'

' Yes.' Suddenly she knew that she had.

'And?' he queried, before she had time to carry on.

'I'd like to stay—if you still want me.'

He put down his cup. 'Then that's settled. Now. I notice our first bookings are end of March and beginning of April. That gives us roughly four weeks before we start getting busy.'

'We shan't be in full swing, of course, until May, although naturally July and August are the busiest months.'

'So between now and May we'll have time to get the office looking a little less like a gardener's shed and the whole place tidied up a bit.'

'Tidied up?' she queried suspiciously.

'The grass cut, a few tubs of flowers around and some sort of order in the sheds.'

She suppressed a sigh. 'If I may say so, tubs of flowers would only be in the way.'

'We won't put them where they'll be in the way,' he answered firmly. 'As a woman I'd have thought you'd like to see the place looking decorative.'

'It depends what you mean by 'decorative'.' She resisted the temptation to remind him that this was a boatyard, not the entrance to some palatial suite of offices in the middle of London or New York. 'To my mind, a boatyard has a charm all its own, and nature supplies all the embellishments that are necessary.'

There was a silence. 'Nature can always be improved upon or given a helping hand. You should know that,' he answered.

Julia wanted to come back at him again, but felt any further reply on the subject would constitute an argument. He would soon find out, she thought, that tubs of flowers along the water's edge—if that was what he had in mind—would be very much in the way when boats were being pushed off or coming in to moor.

He thanked her for the coffee and rose, and she imagined she saw a faint smile of triumph on his face. He departed, and when she had washed the cups and saucers she went back to the office and answered the mail. When she returned there after lunch she saw that he had signed the ones she had left on her desk for him.

She looked at the clear, neat signature. Roger Leighton. Roger. She decided it suited him without asking herself why.

He came into the room where the radio and television sets were stored just as she was carrying one of them out.

'Where are you going with that?' he asked.

'There's a space in the linen store. I thought they could go in there.'

'And you were going to carry all this lot yourself? Give that to me. You can bring the transistors—though they look a poor lot—and I'd have thought most people had their own.'

She hid a smile as he took the television set from her. It wasn't really heavy. All the sets had only twelve-inch screens. Obviously, he was used to pampering women. Or bossing them. She heard him call out to Andy, and the youth came and began carrying the sets from one place to another. Soon the room was empty.

'I'll have those down, too,' the new boss said, indicating the duckboard shelves. 'They're hideous.'

'For an office, perhaps, but ideal for storage of goods like linen or paper—anything, in fact, which is capable of taking in moisture from the atmosphere.'

'The atmosphere in places where those sort of things are stored shouldn't have moisture in it,' he answered dogmatically. 'Store-rooms should be warm and dry.'

Julia suppressed a sigh. It was all very well to say what should or should not be. Most boatyards started out modestly, their sheds and store-rooms added to as the business grew. The boat-hire business in Norfolk had grown beyond anything envisaged when two men first took out a rowing boat years ago at Wroxham and explored the river Bure and the many inlets and Broads.

Roger Leighton had strolled over to the window and was looking out on to the boatyard.

'I still think this whole set-up should be reorganized. This business of going outside from one place to another —it's ridiculous. The office and store-rooms should all be under one roof—and even the sheds and repair shops connected by a covered-way.'

The business executive talking again, thought Julia. What was the use of arguing with him?

'People who work in and around boatyards get used to popping in and out of doors,' she told him. 'Things are becoming different now, I suppose, with big take-overs, even in the boat-hire business. But most firms were embarked on by the owning of one or more craft and *built up*—not started with huge capitals. Of what use would it be to start rebuilding and reorganizing?'

He turned slowly and looked at her, a flicker of amusement in his eyes.

'You have a good deal to learn about the success-ful running of a business, Miss Barclay. You must always appear to be expanding. A look of prosperity attracts prosperity. Never appear to be content to just jog along. You know all the clichés, I'm sure. "Throw a sprat to catch a mackerel," "money attracts money" and so on. If you're afraid of spending money you'll never make any.'

Julia thought it all sounded revolting. 'Does it never occur to you, Mr Leighton, that there might be some people—if not most of them—in the boat-hire business simply because they love boats—not merely to make money?'

'Nonsense. Everybody likes to make money.'

'But some more than others.'

'Granted. However, for various reasons, we'll just go ahead on the idea of improving the existing office of Wingcraft at the moment. I've found a painter and decorator who can come and start work of the place tomorrow. Once he's done this room you can move in here while he does the outer office. If you would prefer it, of course, you can use the houseboat until it's all done. Or better still, there's a room in the house. Yes, that would be better,' he said with sudden decision. ' We'll transfer the whole lot there for a week or so.'

And without waiting to hear whether she agreed or disagreed he went outside and called to Andy again. Julia would rather have taken her typewriter to the houseboat and carried on there, but she supposed on reflection it would make things rather difficult. He would not feel free to come and go to the houseboat. Quite honestly, she thought this was all something of a nuisance. She admitted that the office needed smartening up, but she would have done it without so much upheaval. On the whole, she was not at all sure that she was going to enjoy working with Roger Leighton after all.

' You'd better come and tell Andy where you want things putting,' he said, coming back into the empty room.

' Yes, of course.'

After all, he was the boss, she told herself as she followed him out, and she had agreed to work for him.

Julia had not been in the house for several weeks, and then only in the hall. Pending the sale of the place she had kept on Mrs Harris who came daily to clean. All the same she was suddenly struck with the dreariness and drabness of both walls and furnishings. She might have been seeing it through Roger Leighton's own eyes.

She directed Andy where to put the filing cabinet and rearranged the furniture to make more space.

' Have you got a few minutes to spare?' Roger Leighton asked, gazing at the walls and ceiling with an expression of distaste.

' I'm at your disposal, of course,' she answered.

' Then come and give me your opinion with regard to

a colour scheme for the living room. I can't stand it as it is much longer.'

Carefully controlling the flood of memories of David which crowded into her heart, Julia followed Roger across the hall. She stood in the doorway for a moment, and as clearly as if he were actually there, she saw David's fair head leaning back on his favourite chair, then sitting at the piano and again bending down to put a fresh log on the open fire.

'The piano is about the only decent thing in the room,' said Roger Leighton, causing her visions to fade.

Julia glanced around the room. It was true. Profits had been ploughed back into the business rather than spent on things like new furniture or other home improvements, and David had spent his spare money on piano music and records.

'There's the record player and the album,' she pointed out.

'Oh yes. But I expect the records are mainly pop.'

A swift anger rose in her. 'Why should you suppose any such thing? There might be some, but in the main they're a very good collection of classics—whole symphonies and concertos. If you don't want them—'

She had been on the point of offering to buy them, but an enquiring look from him caused her to break off.

'Were you—a personal friend of the previous owners?' he asked.

She took a deep dreath. 'Yes, you could say that.'

'Well, I'm sorry. But I hope you're not going to be offended every time I criticize anything that belonged to them or any of their methods—that sort of thing.'

'Of course not. I can take honest criticism either of myself or—or a friend when it's given in the right spirit, but—'

'But—what? Why do you so often break off in mid-sentence?' he demanded.

'All right, since you press me. I was about to say

36

that *you* so often jump to conclusions.'

His eyebrows shot up. ' Don't you ever do that yourself?'

' I suppose so—sometimes.'

He nodded. ' So do we all.' Then, after a pause: ' Right. Then I might keep the record player. Do you play the piano, by the way?'

' A little.'

' What do you mean by a little?'

She suppressed a sigh, wishing he would stop asking personal questions and talk about the décor of the room, if that was what he had brought her here for.

' I suppose it depends on what your musical requirements are,' she told him. ' I'm not up to professional standard, otherwise I wouldn't be working here, would I? I suppose you might say I can play moderately difficult things reasonably well, but not always perfectly.'

' Fair enough. Come in and play any time you like. I don't play myself, but I like to hear someone else— barring five-finger exercises. Now then, let me hear your ideas about decorating and furnishing this room.'

Julia glanced around. Homely was the kindest word which could be said about it. There was a large, old-fashioned sofa and a couple of heavy armchairs, a television set of the old cabinet variety, but no books. Neither David nor his father had been great readers. In the spring, summer and autumn, their spare time had been little enough, and in the winter David preferred either to play the piano or listen to the records while his father read the local and national newspapers from cover to cover. And for the short time Julia had stayed with them, she had been content to listen to David's playing, too, or to take a turn in playing herself, though her performance lacked the brilliance of his.

' Dreaming again?' came Roger Leighton's voice.

She started. She must have spent more time with her thoughts than she realized. ' I'm sorry. But look, Mr Leighton, why don't you get a decorator in and ask his

37

opinion?'

'Perhaps I will, but I want your ideas and opinions, too. I want the room—in fact the whole house—to have a feminine touch. It's a little too masculine at the moment even for me.'

A feminine touch. Why? If he was thinking of getting married why couldn't his future wife choose her own furniture and colour schemes? Julia was sure she herself wouldn't want another woman choosing for *her*. But perhaps he was planning a surprise. He folded his arms and waited, a look of resigned patience on his face.

Julia suppressed another sigh and glanced around the room again, frowning slightly.

'It's really a little difficult to know what to do with this room,' she said. 'It isn't really big enough to accommodate a grand piano and leave space for much else. A lot depends, of course, on how much entertaining you intend doing.'

'Well, some, naturally, but I go for the small, intimate parties rather than filling my house with people I'm merely acquainted with.'

Julia smiled faintly. They would have that much in common anyway.

'Do you know what I once thought I'd like to do with this room? But you probably wouldn't agree,' she said.

'Try me.'

'Well, the dining room is next door. It's been very little used, and I don't suppose you'll sit in state there very often alone. I think it would be a good idea to knock part of the room down and have an open plan dining/sitting room. Make the division about here—' she indicated the end of the piano—'have the same carpet throughout, preferably in some rich dark colour, with pale walls. Velvet curtains for winter, and perhaps none in the summer on the dining side with the french windows looking out on to what *ought* to be the garden. Lighter armchairs than these,' she went on, touching

38

one of the present cumbersome ones, ' and a long settee, possibly of cane. I'm sure you'll want to have a new dining room suite, too. I saw a lovely one in town the other day. It had a name and a very unusual design in mahogany. The table had two sets of centre legs—if you know what I mean—'

' Yes, I know what you mean. '

'—and the sideboard was bow-shaped with long, slender legs. The chairs too, were beautifully designed.'

' You appear to have very good taste,' he remarked. ' And I think your idea of knocking these two rooms into one is excellent. But I'll have to do something about the heating. I hate these radiators. They spoil the appearance of a room, don't you think?'

Julia agreed with him and excused herself, escaping to the study to put things to rights there. Seeing a mental picture of the finished rooms had put a tight band of pain around her heart. If only she had been making these plans with David! She had been a complete idiot to agree to staying on here. On her own, it wouldn't have been so bad. But with another man in David's place—

She shook off her depression and went back across to the office to see what else required to be brought over. She found Max there, glancing all around and running his hand through his hair.

' What on earth is going on?' he asked. ' Moving house?'

' More or less. Mr Leighton is having the whole place redecorated and furnished—and the other room made into an office for himself,' she told him.

' Lord! Executive style. And where are you going to work in the meantime?' She told him and he pulled a face. ' That'll be awkward. I don't like the idea of having to knock on his door every time I want to see you.'

' You'll have to learn to come out of working hours. It won't take long, not more than a week or so, but in

39

any case, I don't really think you should come and see me when I'm working. I'm not exactly my own boss.'

He gave her a questioning glance. 'Do you mean you've decided to stay on after all? I thought you said over the phone last night that nothing would induce you to?'

'Yes, I know. And I did write out my notice and hand it to him, but—'

'But he got to work on you?'

She averted her head. 'Well, it was obvious that he wanted me to stay on. And to tell you the truth, I didn't really want to go.'

He grinned. 'That makes two of us. I didn't want you to go, either. You know why, don't you?'

Julia frowned. 'Max, I wish you wouldn't say things like that.'

'Why not, for heaven's sake?'

She opened her desk drawer and began to collect her few personal belongings together.

'You know how I felt about David. It isn't very easy to forget. Besides—'

He moved swiftly to her side and put an arm about her shoulders.

'Darling, this is nonsense.' He lifted up her chin and said softly but firmly: '*David is dead*. You must accept that. You can't love a man for ever.'

'Can't you? You don't understand.'

'But I *do*,' he insisted. 'Really I do. I knew David, too, you know. He was a friend of mine. He wouldn't want you to pine for ever.'

'I'm *not* pining!'

Her lips quivered. She *wasn't* pining. It was just that she needed him so. A love did not die just because the person died, and while she still loved David this way there was no room in her heart for anyone else. Not in the same way.

Max pulled her round gently to face him, and feeling the need for comfort she leaned on him for a brief

40

moment. There was a footstep outside and, inevitably, Roger Leighton appeared in the doorway. Raggedly, Julia moved out of Max's arms. She had not felt like this about David for quite some time. Going into the house, seeing his piano again must have brought everything back, she concluded fleetingly.

'Is anything wrong?' Roger Leighton asked, searching her face.

She shook her head swiftly. 'No, no. It's—all right.'

His sympathetic expression vanished and he turned to go out again.

'Did you—want me for something, Mr Leighton?' she called out.

He turned and gave Max a hard stare. 'It's not important,' he answered. 'When you're free will do.'

He strode away, and Max gave an amused smile. 'Well, well. Different from his attitude yesterday,' he remarked.

Julia sighed. 'Having put me in the position of his assistant he would hardly reprimand me as though I were a typist.'

'As his assistant, eh? That's interesting,' he said thoughtfully.

'Is it?' she queried absentmindedly.

He nodded. 'Let's go over to the houseboat and have a cup of tea. You look as though you need one.'

Julia glanced at her watch. It was near the time she usually had tea anyway and she certainly felt she could do with a cup. She led the way across the snow-covered ground, remarking that she would be glad to see the end of the snow.

'According to the weather forecast there's a thaw on the way,' Max informed her. He stretched out on the studio couch and watched her as she made the tea and poured it. 'You know, I don't think you're all that keen on working with—or for—Leighton, are you?'

'I don't know,' she answered, still feeling ragged

somehow. 'One minute he seems all right, another, I could hit him.'

Max grunted. 'I should think he can be pretty maddening most of the time. Is he going to—run the business, then?' he asked. 'Or sort of come and go and leave things to you?'

Julia shook her head. 'He intends to make a go of it.'

Max grimaced. 'Got a lot of big ideas, has he?'

'Some,' she answered briefly, reluctant to discuss her boss with Max.

He laughed. 'I can imagine! These city types—it doesn't make sense. An oil magnate, more or less, trying to run a boat-hire and boatbuilding business. I don't think he'll last five minutes.'

'I don't see why not. And if he did fail, it wouldn't reflect very favourably on me, would it?'

Max looked up at her and gave a slow smile. 'There might still be a chance of being the owner if you—go about it the right way.'

Julia frowned. 'What on earth do you mean?'

He shrugged. 'Surely you don't want me to spell it out for you?'

'Yes, I do. I want to know what you mean.'

He laughed shortly. 'Oh, for heaven's sake! All I mean is that if you leave him alone and don't spoon-feed him, drop a hint here and there that you'd still like to buy the place—'

'He knows that already, and I can hardly work for him and watch him do something disastrous without saying a word.'

'It needn't be anything disastrous, as you put it. But I don't see why you should run his business *for* him. Just let him make his own decisions—he'll soon run his neck into a noose.'

Julia did not like this kind of talk at all. 'I shall just do my job as usual, Max. What else *can* I do? I certainly couldn't keep silent if I thought he was doing something detrimental to the business. If he ever turns down my advice or suggestions, it will be a different matter, of course.'

Max shook his head. 'Honestly, Julia, you're being very short-sighted. This boatyard is only a hobby—a sideline—for a man like Leighton. He's not serious about it. Let him trip up a few times, and he'll soon pack it in. And meanwhile, make him one or two offers.'

'I'm sorry, Max,' she said firmly. 'What you suggest is quite impossible. I shall do my best to help him. As a matter of fact, I wouldn't like to see him trip up or fail in any way. If he finds the life doesn't suit him or he decides to sell for any reason I shall certainly ask for the first option. Beyond that—no.'

Max finished his tea and stood up. 'I still think you're being silly *and* obstinate. However, what about tonight? We could have a bite to eat somewhere if you like, or have a look around and see what's on at the pictures.'

But Julia felt put off Max's company for the present. 'Not tonight, if you don't mind, Max. It's been a— ragged sort of day, and I'd just as soon stay in and have an early night. Some other time.'

He shrugged. 'All right.' But on his way to the door of the boathouse he turned. 'I've offended you by what I said, haven't I?'

She shook her head, not wanting to make an issue out of it. 'Not really.'

He laughed briefly and put a hand on her shoulder. 'You took me too seriously. I didn't want you to do anything your conscience wouldn't let you. I know how badly you wanted this place, that's all. I'd still like to see it in your hands, and I feel pretty certain that, one of these days, it will be. I'll give you a ring—and maybe we'll have dinner at the Staithe at the week-end.'

She smiled and nodded and he left. She didn't want

to quarrel with Max. He was just about the only friend she had at present. At home, of course, she had had lots of friends. But in this part of the country it took time. If you did not meet people in the course of your work—and Julia didn't—you had to join a club or a society, and that was something she had never got around to, probably never would.

She washed the cups and saucers feeling restless and unsettled. She would be glad when the snow had gone and the busy season arrived. She would then have no time for mooning.

She went back to the office and collected together the few remaining items from her desk drawer and took them across to the house. Roger Leighton was nowhere to be seen as she pushed open the glass vestibule door and went into the study. Andy had brought everything across he could lay his hands on and had piled it all higgledy-piggledy in the middle of the room.

She set to work on sorting it out and as she picked up the telephone directory from the floor she saw what looked like a white card. She picked it up and turned it over, to see that it was a photograph. She had never seen it before, yet it was vaguely familiar. It was the photograph of a woman—young, attractive, well groomed.

Then suddenly Julia recognised her. It was the same face Roger Leighton had drawn when he had been doodling this morning.

CHAPTER THREE

As Julia stared at the picture Roger Leighton came into the room. She glanced up swiftly and held the photograph out to him.

' I think this must be yours.'

He took it from her, his face taut. ' Where did you find it?' he asked sharply.

' On the floor just now. You—must have dropped it,' she answered, turning away and continuing with what she was doing. Out of the corner of her eye she saw him put the photograph in his pocket. How had he come to drop it? she wondered. He didn't look the kind of man who would continually take out a photograph and keep looking at it, no matter how much in love he might be.

' Do you want any help?' he asked suddenly. ' It all looks the most frightful muddle.'

' I can manage, thanks,' she answered. ' I'll soon get it all sorted out. Do you want me to set up two desks— one for each of us?'

He nodded. ' You might as well, though I'm not expecting to spend much time in here. I—take it your —friend has gone?' he remarked, with what seemed a swift change of subject.

She nodded. ' I've—told him he mustn't come to see me during working hours.'

' Oh, why?' he queried unexpectedly.

' Because I—don't feel it's right. You're not paying me to have social calls.'

He gave a faint smile of amusement. ' I appreciate your being conscientious, but you're not being paid by the hour. I wouldn't have asked you to stay on if I didn't think I could trust you to use your discretion in these matters. Are you—er—by any chance seeing him this evening?'

She gave him a surprised look and shook her head.
'I'm planning an early night.'

'What do you call early?'

'Oh, bed somewhere around ten o'clock with a good book. Why do you ask?'

'I was wondering if you'd take pity on a stranger in a strange land, so to speak. This place depresses me entirely at the moment. Would you come out and have dinner with me?' His lips curved again in amusement. 'I promise to bring you back by ten.'

'Are you serious?' she asked dubiously.

'Of course I'm serious. Why shouldn't I be?'

She skirted that question. She was not sure why she had asked it.

'Very well, yes. I'd love to come, thanks.'

'Good, I'll give you a call around seven,' he said briskly, and went out.

Julia scarcely knew whether she was pleased at the invitation or not, or whether she could justifiably feel flattered. As she was the only woman to hand, and at present the house was rather a depressing place in which to eat, she decided she could hardly feel flattered. And pleased? She had not really been looking forward to another evening alone. She had had so many since David had died, in spite of Max being around.

As she brought some kind of order in what used to be the Hargreaves' study she began to realise for the first time how lonely she really had been. She realized, too, that though she had been grateful for Max's friendship, she only liked his company for any length of time when she was in a particularly good humour. The slightest thing put her off him. She hadn't wanted to see him tonight, for instance, yet she was quite happy to go out to dinner with Mr Leighton. It even mattered to her what she wore, but she told herself that this was only because she felt he would be accustomed to taking out smart and well-dressed women and she wanted to be equal to the occasion.

46

Naturally, as she searched her wardrobe an hour or so later she did not appear to have a thing to wear. A greater part of her wardrobe was still at home because since coming to Norfolk she had not dressed up a very great deal. She was still young enough to dress informally and, spending most of her time around the boatyard, she wore slacks and sweaters a good deal anyway.

Tonight, however, she felt she needed to strike exactly the right note—whatever that was. Casual elegance, not appearing to have dressed up too much. Her hand closed on a dress she had bought for Christmas one year and had only worn a few times. It was in corduroy velvet, dove grey with a froth of white lace at the neck and sleeves. She took it out, and for a moment knew a sharp stab of pain. She had been wearing this dress when she had first met David. Quickly, she put it back on the rail. She couldn't wear that. She simply couldn't!

Then: 'Don't be silly, darling. Wear it. Go out and have fun,' she seemed to hear David say.

She smiled to herself and reached into the wardrobe again and brought the dress out. That was just the sort of thing he *would* have said. She didn't know about the evening being ' fun ', but at any rate she ought to stop being so silly.

She pinned up her hair and had a bath, and it was with a feeling of pleasure that she slipped on the little grey dress and smoothed it over her hips. It still fitted her perfectly, and looked exactly right for the occasion. Was she attaching too much importance to the evening? she asked herself. After all, it could barely be called a social engagement. He simply wanted to go out to eat and someone to go with him. Any other woman would have done just as well. All the same, he *was* her boss, she argued with herself, and the first time out with any man was an occasion. First time? She gave a wry smile. It might also be the last.

Roger Leighton knocked on her door at a little after

47

seven, and she slipped on her simulated pony-skin coat and a pair of white gloves. When she opened the door she was gratified to see a swift raising of his dark brows.

' Very nice.' Then his glance went to her thin shoes. ' But stay there for a minute and I'll back the car up a little closer.'

She watched with some amusement as he brought the car almost to the door, then put down a rubber car mat for her to step on to avoid the snow-covered ground.

' Thank you, Sir Walter,' she couldn't resist saying.

He opened the car door for her and helped her in, then slammed the door and went swiftly round to the other side.

' When one meets up with a lady, one tries to behave like a gentleman,' he answered, starting up the car.

Miraculously, the car pulled out of the snow again without too much fierce revving, and they were soon back on to hard ground. A glance at the dark grey car-coat he was wearing with its rich fur collar and she was glad she had chosen to dress up a little bit, and there was no doubt about the expensiveness of his car. She leaned back and let the luxury and comfort wash over her. It was a long time since she had felt so completely relaxed.

' Have you any particular preference of a place to eat?' he asked after a moment or two.

She shook her head and snuggled still further into her seat.

' I'll leave it entirely to you—unless, of course, you want my advice.'

He gave her an amused glance. ' No, I think I know of a place. The hotel in Norwich where I stayed over-night will be fine until I've had time to look around further.'

He was a wonderfully smooth driver. Julia closed her eyes. She had almost forgotten what it was like to be taken out in such style. Her own car had only been small, David's had been a shooting brake, and they

48

had seldom dined out in style the short time they had known each other. In style. She laughed to herself. To Roger Leighton this was an ordinary 'popping out to dinner' evening. Nothing special.

A sudden squealing of brakes brought her upright.

'Sorry,' murmured the man at the wheel. 'It was the clot in front of me. Were you asleep?'

'Not really. Just relaxing. Such a comfortable car —and such smooth driving—'

'Until now.'

She gave the flicker of a smile. 'Never mind. You can't hope to go through life without being brought up short every now and then.'

'Who'd want to?' he retorted. 'But I don't like to be taken off guard.'

'Oh, I see—' she said slowly.

'What do you see?' he asked, pulling up at a traffic light.

She felt an almost foreign sense of mischief bubbling inside her. 'You like life to be a challenge, but in general *you* like to be the one who's doing the challenging—not other people.'

'Are you trying to tell me that I'm aggressive?'

'No—o, not in so many words. I simply think you're the sort of person who likes to go out and meet life and to be girded to meet challenges.'

He grunted. 'I'll have to think about that one. At the moment I have to concentrate on my driving.'

She smiled in the darkness of the car. 'I *am* taking rather unfair advantage. I'll say no more until you can give proper attention to conversation.'

'Thanks,' he said with a hint of sarcasm.

He dropped her off at what was unquestionably the best hotel in town, and she waited in the foyer while he parked his car. Seh knew that he would be at least five minutes, as new traffic regulations prevented parking outside the hotel, so she settled before the log-effect fire. What she was not prepared for was the appearance

49

of Max, and the sight of him caused her acute embarrassment. He stared at her.

'What on earth are you doing here, Julia?' he asked. 'I thought you wanted an early night?' He dropped into a chair opposite.

'So I did—and I still do.'

'But you said you didn't want to come out at all. At least, that was the impression I got. So why—'

'I changed my mind, that's all, Max. I'm sorry.'

Her glance flicked to the door where Roger Leighton's tall figure was pushing a way in.

Max turned swiftly and saw him. 'Oh, I see. That's the way the wind blows, is it?'

'I don't know what you mean,' she answered, slightly annoyed. 'He asked me out to dinner and—well, I—didn't feel I could refuse.'

He gave her a most calculating look. 'You mean you didn't want to.'

Roger strode past them to deposit his coat, but there was no doubt he had seen them.

'Max, I've said I'm sorry. When you asked me I just didn't feel like coming out. Later I—did, that's all.'

He stood up as a mini-skirted girl came through the glass doors.

'Well, it's an ill wind, Julia. Here comes my date. Have a nice evening.'

Julia thanked him, feeling distinctly nettled. What had he meant exactly by the reference to an 'ill wind'? Possibly trying to save his pride by hinting that he preferred the other girl anyway. And obviously he had put some interpretation of his own on her change of mind.

Roger returned. 'Would you like a drink here—or would you prefer the cocktail lounge?'

She shook her head as she watched Max and his companion go into the cocktail lounge.

'Here, please.'

'You—wouldn't like to go and find somewhere else to eat?' he queried, glancing in the same direction.

'It's all right,' she told him. 'It's rather unfortunate Max choosing to come here too, but the damage—if any —is done now.'

He ordered their drinks, then asked: 'Why do you say, *if any*?'

'Naturally, he's rather annoyed that I declined his invitation, then accepted yours. But I think only his pride is hurt, and that he'll soon recover.'

'I can imagine. About his pride being hurt, I mean. But look—if it's going to prove too embarrassing, we can go elsewhere. I wouldn't like the evening to be spoilt.'

She smiled suddenly. 'It won't be. I didn't know the girl he was with, but she looked very attractive.'

Roger grimaced. 'Not to my taste. Clothes too short, hair too long, lack of character in the face.'

Julia laughed. 'You deduced all that from the back?'

He eyed her speculatively, as if suspecting she was having fun at his expense.

'I had a good enough look at her face from the front just before she and Windham turned into the hotel—and her clothes and hair were visible from the back.'

Laughter ticked over inside Julia. 'Point taken. So you don't approve of short skirts. Or long hair.'

'I don't like clothes as short as hers, at any rate. Yours are just about right,' he answered, glancing at her hemline and her slim legs. 'And I like to see a woman's hair looking as though it's cared for and with some semblance of style.'

She smiled broadly. 'Like mine?'

His glance flicked over her fair hair, layered to a medium length, kept manageable by the healthy, outdoor life she led, plus regular applications of conditioner.

'Yes,' he said. 'Like yours.'

She was glad that the waiter came with their drinks. She had begun to feel a little embarrassed, realizing she

had been virtually asking for compliments. All the
same, it was rather nice to know he approved of her
appearance, and she was sure he was not the sort of
man to pay compliments if he did not mean them. But
what did he think of her as a person? Perhaps it was
too soon for him to tell, and that was one question she
would not ask him.

'As a matter of interest,' he said, after a pause, 'why
did you turn Windham down and then accept my invitation?'

She gave him a mischievous glance. 'When he asked
me I just didn't feel like going out. You made me
change my mind—which says a great deal for your
powers of persuasion.'

'Mm,' he said thoughtfully. 'You wouldn't have
come if you hadn't really wanted to, I hope.'

'No, I wouldn't,' she assured him.

He smiled suddenly. 'May I call you Julia?'

'Of course,' she answered swiftly.

'And my name is Roger.'

She nodded. 'Roger. A family name?'

'No. The family name is Charles. Fortunately, I
was given two names and as soon as I was at an age to
think things out for myself, I insisted on being called
by my own choice of name—Roger.'

She would have liked him to elaborate, to have said
why he objected to the family name. She felt sure there
was much more significance than mere dislike of a
Christian name. But for that very reason she did not
ask.

'And at what age *did* you start to think for yourself?'
she quizzed with a smile.

'With regard to the family business—which is tied up
with the name—from the age of about ten,' he told her.

'Did that mean that you—disapproved of the business
as well as the name?' she asked cautiously.

'No-o, not really. I simply wanted to have a separate
identification. I didn't become actively involved with

52

the business until I was eighteen.'

As he spoke his face sobered and she wondered what the situation was between him and the oil business. Had he really, as Max had suggested, quarrelled with his father? Of a happy, united family herself, she hoped not. To her way of thinking there were only two reasons left for his leaving the business to come to Norfolk. One was a general dissatisfaction with the oil company, the other a broken love affair.

'Shall we go in to dinner?' he asked, as she set down her empty sherry glass.

'Yes, of course.'

She rose, conscious that her previous light-hearted mood had changed. He too seemed to have become rather grave, and she wished they had kept his family and the oil business out of the conversation.

They were shown to a table for two and menus placed before them. It was plain from the way Roger questioned the waiter and consulted her taste that he was well accustomed to going out and about, to dining at the best places. He seemed to know instinctively the right food and wine to choose and quickly shook off his serious mood of a few minutes ago.

'Well, tell me a little about yourself,' he said as they began the first course.

Reluctant to talk about the double tragedy of David and his father's death she said lamely: 'There's not much to tell.'

He gave her an amused, admonishing look. 'Come now, I'm sure you can do better than that. You'll have me thinking you have a shady past. You're not a native of Norfolk, anyhow, are you?' he prompted.

It was silly to be so reticent about herself. There was no need to talk about David if she did not wish to. And so she told him about her parents and the Kentish fruit farm.

'It must be very lovely, especially in the spring,' he commented.

53

'Oh, it is. It's really beautiful. I love it.'

'Then why—'

It was inevitable, and she could not really understand her reluctance to speak of David.

'Why did I come to Norfolk? I met David—Mr Hargreaves' son. We became friendly and I came for a holiday. Then we—I decided to stay.'

'You and he—?' he queried hesitantly.

'We became engaged.'

'Oh. Oh, I'm sorry. I shouldn't have asked. Do forgive me. It must have been—terrible for you.'

Suddenly she felt her food would choke her, yet at the same time she told herself it was ridiculous to feel this way. She could not understand herself, except that, while not actually still grieving for David, the gap left in her life was greater than she had even realized.

'Tell me what you think of the wine,' Roger said in a quiet voice.

She took a sip and forced a smile. 'It's very good.'

She drank a little more and found she could continue the meal better.

'How long since you went home?' Roger Leighton asked her, after a minute or two.

'Christmas.'

'Why don't you go again? Take a little holiday while the work on the office is being done. I imagine you won't want to go when things get busy.'

She smiled genuinely at that. 'How nicely you put it,' she told him. 'But I can't very well go now. You've only just come.'

'The place won't fall apart because you're not here,' he told her.

'I suppose not. Perhaps I could go for a long week-end,' she suggested.

'It's entirely up to you. I just thought you needed a change.'

'You're very kind.'

He looked as though he might deny it, but a waitress

54

came to clear away their empty plates and serve the second course. Julia noticed that Max and his friend had now taken their places at one of the tables. Roger saw them too, and gave Julia a questioning look.

'You don't seem to mind.'

'Why should I?'

He smiled. 'That's answer enough. You don't look exactly heartbroken. And I'm glad. I wouldn't have said he was your type at all.'

'That's interesting,' she answered. 'What makes you say so—and what sort of man do you think *is* my type?'

He thought for a moment. 'The answer to the first question can be very brief. It's a sort of instinct I have that a man like that could never make you happy. One thing being a director of Melloid has taught me is to judge character from the look of a person. I've met so many in the course of business.'

'Aren't you ever mistaken?'

He shook his head. 'Very rarely. A person you can trust looks straight at you.'

But she was not so easily convinced. 'But wouldn't that be one of the tricks of a con man—to look you straight in the eye while planning to do you down?'

'Oh yes. But there are other things. A confidence man is generally too smooth, agrees with you too readily, never gets annoyed. A person you can trust has depth.'

Julia shook her head swiftly. 'But you can't tell just by looking at a person whether he has depth or not.'

'You can, in a way. There's a certain look in the eyes, in the set of the jaw, in a man's—or woman's— whole expression.'

Julia had to concede that he could be right. Hadn't she come to some conclusions about Roger himself from across the auction room? It was true she had not been able to put her assessment of him to a real test, but—

'*That* man,' Roger was saying with quiet emphasis,

55

eyeing Max across the room, 'is as selfish as hell and as conniving as a fox, if I'm any judge.'

Julia was conscious of a sense of dismay. It was rather frightening to meet a man who judged the character of people so ruthlessly.

'I don't see how you can possibly tell,' she protested. 'And personally, I'd hate to be judged in such a way.'

His eyes widened. 'But you wouldn't be judged that way. The worst one could say about you would be that you have a mind and a will of your own—and that can't be called a fault.'

'It could be,' she argued.

He shook his head. 'You tend to fly off the handle, partly because you're so honest. But you also have a— strong sentimental streak in you.'

She felt her cheeks warming. 'You sound like a character-reading act at a—' She broke off, suddenly realising how rude she was being. 'I'm sorry.'

His jaw tightened for a second, then his lips curved into a slight smile. 'That's all right. I didn't intend to get so personal, but at least you've confirmed what I said. You tend to fly off the handle.'

'I've already said I'm sorry,' she flashed out. Then she saw the humorous side and laughed. 'You're perfectly right, of course.'

'There you are. Honest, too. I told you I was an expert.'

Mischief stirred once more as she looked at him across the table. 'Of course I only fly off the handle when someone provokes me.'

'And I provoked you. You must learn not to let your feelings show so much.'

'Why? I was brought up to express my feelings freely. How else can the human race get to know each other? There's far too much surface politeness, people pretending they don't care about things. Why should we be afraid to show our emotions?'

She could see from his expression that he did not agree

56

with her and at heart, she did not fully mean what she had said. There were times when control was necessary. He said more or less what she expected him to say.

'Emotions can get out of hand if they're not controlled. Mass hysteria, for example. It isn't wise to bottle up *sorrow* too much, of *course*. I think everyone more or less agrees on that.' He gave her an odd look which at that moment there wasn't time to interpret. He went on : ' But in conceding the need for free expression, there is another factor to be considered. The effect on other people.'

Conscience smote her and she was aware of a hurt feeling mixed with resentment that he had knowingly or unknowingly administered a dose of medicine.

'You mean—I say what I think without considering the feelings of others?' she queried bluntly.

His eyes opened wide. 'I didn't mean that at all. You're sensitive as well as being sentimental. And before you protest about that, I mean it as a compliment. I should say you're only too well aware of the feelings of others. I was referring to those people who take freedom of expression to extremes and to blazes with the effect on either individuals or the world in general. Rioters, demonstrators, warmongers and murderers, for instance. I'm quite sure that in allowing you a certain amount of freedom of expression your parents didn't let you have all your way. A certain amount of self-control is essential. If you're not taught it as a child, life can well be hell when you grow up.'

He tackled his food for a few minutes as if he felt he had said too much, or as if he had been speaking personally and wished he hadn't. But taking a glance at his face, she would have thought he was a man who had learned to control his feelings very well indeed. Perhaps a little too well.

He looked up suddenly and smiled. 'We're getting too serious, aren't we? I was supposed to be telling

57

you what kind of man was your type.'

'So you were. Do tell me. I can hardly wait to hear.'

He took a sip of his wine. 'Let me see now. One thing is certain. You'd need a man whose mind matched your own—lively and intelligent. But his brain would have to be slightly superior to yours. You wouldn't want it other. And he would have to be firm with you at times.'

'Really?' she mocked.

'Yes, really. You need taking in hand.'

'By some man?'

'By some man,' he reiterated. 'And for your own good.'

'The dominant, masterful male!'

He eyed her without smiling. 'Call it what you will. You need protecting from men like that—' again his glance went in Max's direction '—who would break that sensitive heart of yours, leave you mentally unsatisfied and be quite incapable of shouldering the responsibilities of married life.'

Julia eyed him rather uncertainly. He was either paying her some very great compliments or simply heartily disliked Max.

She gave him an amused smile. She felt it would never do to take him too seriously.

'When—or if ever—you meet a man willing to take on the job, perhaps you'll let me know. Meanwhile, I'll have to get along the best way I can,' she said lightly.

There was a short silence, then he asked unexpectedly: 'What sort of man was David Hargreaves?'

She felt as though she'd been dealt a blow on the heart. She drew in a painful breath and felt the blood drain from her face.

'I—I'd rather not answer that,' she said stiffly. Then a feeling of exquisite tenderness took possession of her. Dear David. Why shouldn't she talk about him? 'It's

—difficult to say just what kind of man he was,' she said softly. 'He was one who could both excite me and give me a sense of peace, whom I could admire as well as—love, a man of gentleness and of strength, a man without whom—'

She broke off, suddenly aware of the scrutiny of the man across the table. For a few moments she had forgotten the existence of anyone else. *A man without whom I never thought I could exist,* she had been about to say, until she had felt the magnetism of the man sitting opposite her. It occurred to her now that this evening was the very first time she had felt natural since that ghastly day when David had met with his accident.

'I'm—sorry,' she said swiftly. 'I—got carried away.'

'So I noticed,' he answered, his face set in an expression she could not read. Then he added, 'He was evidently quite a man, and almost impossible to compete with, I imagine.'

'As far as I'm concerned, yes, but whether he was my " type " or not as outlined by you—'

Her thoughts took over. David had been intelligent enough to run a boat-hire business. Whether superior to her own intelligence she would find it impossible to say. But firm—and by that she supposed Roger Leighton had meant masterful—he had not shown any evidence that she could recall. He had had no need to. But one did not love a man for mind or capabilities so much as what he did to you. She and David had liked each other immediately. Some might have called it love at first sight. Of one thing she was certain. From their first meeting until his fatal accident a few months later they had been absolutely everything to each other.

'I think it's time to change the subject,' came Roger's voice brusquely.

She started. But she agreed. The conversation had become much too personal.

'Tell me about the oil business,' she said. 'Is it

really anything like that well-known television series?'

He nodded. 'It is, as a matter of fact. At least, in some respects.'

'And were you on the engineering side or—'

'No, sales. But I don't really want to talk about oil, if you don't mind. I came to Norfolk to get away from it. I'd much rather talk about the Broads. The very sound of the name has long held a fascination for me. Why are they called that, by the way? They're really sort of lakes shooting off from the rivers.'

'Perhaps the name just evolved—a broad stretch of water. They're man-made, you know, caused by digging out peat, ages ago.' Then: 'Have you ever taken out a Broads yacht or cruiser for a holiday?' she asked.

'A yacht a couple of times—not as often as I would have liked.'

'I suppose business kept you pretty busy,' she said, though in the back of her mind was the thought that perhaps the woman in his life did not like sailing.

He said, 'Yes,' briefly, then after a pause went on to discuss the sail craft of their own fleet, asking her about her own sailing prowess and which boat she used.

'A half-decker with lug sail,' she told him promptly. 'They're ideal for solo sailing—so easy to manage.'

'But not much "fun", is it, sailing alone?' he queried.

She smiled a little. 'Sometimes there's no option.'

'True, but if there *is* someone around—'

She nodded, thinking of David again. With the right person sailing was more than 'fun'. It was sheer heaven. She and David had planned a honeymoon on a two-berth auxiliary yacht.

Roger Leighton broke into her thoughts, this time talking about the business, that he would like to encourage sailing by having more yachts for hire.

At this she felt once more the urge to tease him. 'That would *not* be very good business.'

60

She expected he would realise that she was joking, but he didn't. He took her seriously and the conversation was not quite as pleasant as it had been previously. They took their coffee in the hotel lounge and Julia noticed his glance go to the clock several times, almost as if he were wanting time to pass. At nine-thirty he suggested it was time to be going.

'I promised to get you back for ten,' he added.

He rose, not giving her the opportunity of changing her mind even if she had wanted to.

It had been a mixed sort of evening, Julia thought as she sat back in the dimness of his car. If it were not for a certain reserve and unaccountable changes of mood he could be an interesting, even an exciting man. At this thought she experienced a faint twinge of conscience, of disloyalty to the memory of David. This was the first time she had taken any interest in another man, as a man, since his death. It was odd that until this evening she had avoided talking about him. Now she found she wanted to. Why, she could not explain, except that she felt almost as if she were being released from a kind of bondage.

It was not until Roger turned into the boatyard that she realised neither of them had spoken all the way home. Apparently he also had been engrossed in his thoughts.

'Well, here we are,' he said, glancing at the clock on the dashboard. 'Dead on time. If you'll give me your key I'll open your door for you.'

'It's all right, I can—' But the words, *I can manage* died in her throat. He was not the kind of man one should say that to. He would not appreciate independence in a woman.

As if to prove her right he ignored her half-finished sentence and held out his hand. With a feeling of amusement she rummaged in her bag and put the key into his palm. In a second he was out of the car, had unlocked the door of the houseboat and was holding the

61

car door open for her.

He helped her out and she thanked him. 'Would you care to come in for a coffee?'

'Er—no, thanks. I have some letters to write, and I mustn't rob you of your beauty sleep.'

More disappointed than she felt she should have been, she pushed open the door of the houseboat and stepped inside.

'Goodnight, then—'

'Julia—'

She turned hopefully. Another half hour of his company over a cup of coffee would round off the evening very nicely.

But all he said was: 'Thanks for turning what would have been a very dull evening into an extremely pleasant one.'

To Julia's ears it sounded stilted and conventional. She murmured her own thanks and said goodnight once more before closing the door.

For a little while after hearing his car drive the few yards to his house and garage, Julia battled raggedly with a sense of dissatisfaction, but gradually she relaxed and smiled to herself as she recalled some of their conversation. In all, she went to bed in a happier frame of mind than she had known for a very long time.

During the night there was a change of wind direction, and a gradual thaw set in. For three days rain came down, accompanied by high winds. The workmen moved into the office and Julia squelched her way to and from the house to work in the temporary office there. She saw very little of Roger. He seemed to be off on some business of which she knew nothing, and when she did see him he had very little to say to her. Julia began to wonder whether he had regretted taking her out to dinner. Perhaps from now on he wanted there to be strictly a boss-employee relationship between them. It was all useless conjecture, of course, and she told herself it didn't matter to her in the slightest what he had in mind. All the same she would be glad when the busy season began, though even Easter was still some weeks away.

On Thursday evening however, as she was putting things away at the end of the day, he came into the study / office.

' Have you thought any more about my suggestion of getting away for a week-end or so?' he asked.

She shook her head.

' Why not?' he demanded. ' Can't you tear yourself away from the place?'

Her eyes widened at his tone. ' I—don't know what you mean. It's just that I haven't thought about it.'

' Don't you *want* to see your parents?' he asked accusingly.

She had actually been thinking of inviting them to visit her over Easter. There was plenty of room in the houseboat. Quite apart from the Broads, this was a very good area in which to spend a holiday. There were so many places of interest all around, and she knew they would enjoy it.

She looked at Roger Leighton's dark face and wondered what had happened to annoy him.

' I'll look up trains and go this week-end,' she said mildly. She thought she had also better ask him if it was all right for her to invite her parents to stay, and was about to do so when he exploded again.

' Trains? You can't travel by train.'

' That's the only way I'll get there,' she told him. ' I haven't a car at present. I sold it when I wanted to buy the business. I'm afraid I've been using the firm's van for odd trips into town. I shall have to get another car, but meanwhile—'

' You can either get yourself another car or use the van, just as it suits you, but I'm going down to Surrey for the week-end myself. That's why I asked you. I thought we might as well travel down together. I'm sure we can both be spared at the moment, whereas in a few weeks' time neither of us will be able to get away.'

That was true. 'But won't Kent be out of your way?'

'Very little. We could travel down tomorrow afternoon and come back Monday morning. And by the way,' he continued before she could say anything, 'ask Mrs Harris if she'll come in over the week-end and clean up the office after the workmen have left. It would be a good idea, too, to decide where you want things to go and leave some instructions with Andy. You won't want to come back and find everything in a muddle and in the wrong places.'

He nodded and walked away in the manner of one acustomed to taking explicit obedience for granted.

'Yes, sir, certainly, sir,' Julia muttered under her breath.

He was certainly in charge and, if one did not watch out, would also take charge of one's life. But oddly enough the idea did not so much anger as amuse her.

She telephoned her parents to let them know she would be coming, and at three o'clock the following day Andy knocked on the door of the houseboat to tell her that Mr Leighton was waiting for her at the front of the house. The boy insisted on carrying her small case and putting it in the boot of the car. Roger opened the door at the passenger side for her without getting out and they set off towards Norwich.

'I'm picking up another pasenger,' he told her. 'Somebody who works in the oil company.'

'Going all the way, you mean?'

He nodded. 'Hope you don't mind.'

'Of course not. But would you rather I sat in the back? Then you'll be able to talk.'

But he shook his head. 'It doesn't matter. Stay where you are.'

He stopped outside a hotel just inside the city boundary and disappeared into the revolving doors.

64

Julia did not know whether she was glad or sorry that they were to have the company of another man, but on the whole she thought it just as well. Roger Leighton could be stimulating company, as she had learned, but something had happened since that night they had had dinner together, and at present he wasn't very communicative at all.

He seemed to be gone for quite a long time, and she feared they would be in trouble for parking over the limit if he did not come soon. But at last he appeared. Greatly to her surprise he was accompanied by a woman —she had taken it for granted that it would be a man. Roger opened one of the rear doors and thrust a case on to the back seat, then helped the woman in. Julia caught a glimpse of someone fashionably dressed and with a certain ' air '. The whiff of an elusive perfume came faintly to her nostrils as the woman took her seat. As Roger went round to the other side of the car Julia turned to smile at her, but involuntarily her eyes widened in surprise.

It was the woman whose face he had drawn while doodling and in the photograph she had picked up from the floor of the house.

CHAPTER IV

Roger slammed the car door behind him, then half turned in his seat.

'Julia, this is Miss Celia Palmer. Celia—Miss Barclay, my deputy.'

Julia smiled and was about to make some friendly remark, but the other girl took a swift look at her and spoke to Roger.

'Your deputy? Really, darling—'

Roger pulled the self-starter. 'Yes, my deputy, Celia,' he muttered over his shoulder. 'And don't call me darling.'

'All right, dar—Roger, just as you say,' came the answer.

The car slid away from the kerb. Julia stole a sideways glance at Roger's face, but it was a mask. Like many men, he was adept at hiding his feelings. Julia was in no doubt whatever that Celia Palmer was more than merely 'somebody who works in the oil company'. They had once been engaged, she was sure of it. Obviously, the other girl had been so in the habit of calling him darling, she still did so automatically, and though Roger might be angry with her, he must still be in love with her, otherwise why draw her face without realizing he was doing so, and why did he still carry her photograph? Julia also recalled Roger's frequent absences from the boatyard in the past few days. He had been seeing Celia, of course.

But now the silence in the car was both unnatural and uncomfortable. Julia could stand it no longer, and feeling it was up to her to try to ease the strain, she turned to speak to the other girl.

'Have you been staying in Norwich long, Miss Palmer?'

Celia's blue eyes widened, almost as though Julia were

committing an impertinence by speaking to her.

'Just a few days,' she answered coolly.

'And have you enjoyed it? Julia was nothing if not persevering.

There was a pause. For a minute or two Julia thought Celia was not going to reply at all. But then she said, in a grumbling tone:

'It's just about the dreariest place I've ever visited in my whole life. And your weather—'

This, apparently, had been too disgusting for words. Julia's lips curved in amusement.

'Unfortunately, that's something we can't do a thing about. But the rain has been pretty widespread throughout the country. As to Norwich being dreary— well, it depends on what kind of entertainment you want. There are plenty of cinemas and theatres, numerous places where you can dine and dance. And in the summer, Norfolk is absolutely delightful.'

'Really?' came the bored response. Then, as if to cut Julia deliberately out of the conversation: 'Roger, you remember my telling you the other evening about old Shaw? Well, I've suddenly thought—'

She went on to talk shop—Melloid Oil shop. Even though some of it was over Julia's head, she felt sure it was not of any real importance. Roger made only the briefest comments or replies to what she was saying. Then at a traffic light, he turned and said to her,

'I'd rather not talk about Melloid Oil, if you don't mind, Celia, and I shall get all the news while I'm at home.'

After this, Celia lapsed into silence, and as Roger barely spoke for the next fifty or sixty miles, it was a most uneasy journey. They stopped at a wayside hotel for tea and as Julia had anticipated, when they came out to resume the journey, Celia announced that she would sit in the front passenger seat, and did so without waiting to hear whether Julia agreed or not.

Julia fervently hoped that they would not have Celia's

company on the return journey and was heartily thankful when Roger stopped the car outside a flat in Croydon and got out to reach for Celia's suitcase.

Celia stepped slowly out on to the pavement. 'You'll come up and have a drink, won't you, darling?' Julia heard her say.

There was a momentary pause from Roger. 'I'll carry up your case for you, but you know I can't linger. We have a long way to go yet.'

He took her arm and they walked towards the house. Celia did not even glance at Julia, who stared after the two, a mixture of feelings. She was not hurt by the other girl's rudeness, but she did confess to a feeling she could only describe as disappointment that a man like Roger Leighton could ever have been remotely in love with someone so lacking in ordinary good manners.

It seemed quite a long time before Roger re-emerged. 'Sorry for the delay,' he said as he took his seat behind the wheel once more. 'I'm afraid it will be dark before I get you home.'

'That's all right,' she told him, beginning to feel something of a nuisance. 'But you needn't drive me all the way home. You can drop me off at Sevenoaks or Maidstone. I can easily get either a bus or train the rest of the way.'

'Which is the nearest?'

'Maidstone.'

But when they reached Maidstone it was pouring with rain and Roger said he might as well drive her the whole of the way home, brushing all her protestations aside. She gave him route directions as they went along, and as soon as he drew up outside the house, the front door opened.

'You *will* come in and meet Mother and Father, won't you?' she asked.

'Of course.'

As she embraced first her mother, then her father, Julia realized how very homesick she had been. Tears

68

pricked her eyes and she felt as though she had been absent from home for years. Roger was introduced, and Helen Barclay invited him into the living room.

'I know you won't want to be delayed too long,' she said, rather cleverly forestalling him, 'but do come in and sit down for a few minutes at any rate.'

'Thank you, I will,' Roger answered.

Julia's mother led the way while her husband took his daughter's coat and went to hang it up. Julia glanced around the familiar living room with its comfortable chesterfield suite, the white-painted bookshelves crammed with books, the flowers which her mother loved, and the various plants her mother grew herself either from seed or cuttings. It was good to be home.

'Come and sit here beside the fire,' her mother invited Roger. 'And perhaps you'd like a glass of sherry.'

But Roger declined. 'No, no, please don't trouble, Mrs Barclay. I can only stay a minute, and I'd much rather just sit and talk to you. This is a most pleasant room.'

'It's comfortable,' Helen Barclay conceded, then went on to ask him about his own home.

'I don't live with my parents as Julia does,' he told them, and Julia was not really surprised to learn this. 'I have my own flat. Or at least, I did. After this week-end I shall let it to the man who has taken my place in the oil company.'

This gave Helen Barclay a chance to comment on the change he had made buying a boat-hire business. He smiled, and Julia noticed how more and more relaxed he was becoming.

'It's peaceful beyond measure,' he said.

Julia laughed. 'You won't find it so very peaceful when the holiday-makers begin to arrive!'

But she realized that he had meant a different kind of peace than the one she had implied. He gave her a look, but made no answer, and she wondered again what had happened to make him want to change one kind of life for such a completely different one. Had it been anything to do with Celia?

Further speculation was impossible at that moment. Her father came in with some coffee.

'I thought you might just have time for a cup before you leave,' he said. 'Unless, of course, we can prevail upon you to stay and have dinner with us.'

'That's very kind of you, but I'm afraid if I stay to dinner I shall be tempted to linger still longer, and I've arranged to meet someone around nine-thirty. But a cup of coffee would be most welcome.'

Julia flashed a grateful look at her father. He always knew exactly the right thing to do. Why had it seemed so urgent that she should own the boat-hire business? Why hadn't she simply come back home? It appeared so absurd, so unnecessary now.

After about another quarter of an hour of pleasant conversation Roger rose to leave.

'I'm so glad we've had the opportunity of meeting you, Mr Leighton,' Helen Barclay said as she shook hands with him. 'And I hope we shall see you again before long.'

'Monday morning to be exact, Mrs Barclay,' he said smiling. 'I'm calling for Julia to take her back to Norfolk, otherwise she might not have come back at all, the comfortable home she has.'

His joke was well received, at least by Julia's parents. Julia herself was not quite sure about it. He had sounded almost possessive, and she did not want her mother and father to get a wrong impression of their relationship. As it was, her mother said, 'We'll let Julia see you off.'

The rain had ceased now, but Roger would not let her come out. They stood in the vestibule for a few minutes, and Julia thanked him for bringing her home.

'It's been a pleasure,' he answered. 'You have very nice folks, and it was good to meet them. I don't know how you can bear to be away for such long periods.'

70

This seemed to her like an accusation, a very justifiable one, but she did not appreciate it coming from him.

'It makes coming home all the greater pleasure,' she told him. 'And perhaps it will be possible to manage a mid-week visit during the summer. I have my longer holiday during the autumn.'

He nodded. 'I'll be here around ten o'clock on Monday morning, then. Make the most of the week-end.'

Naturally, when she went back into the house, Roger came under discussion for a few minutes, and equally naturally, her mother went to her room for a little chat just before Julia put out her light.

'Well, dear, how are you *really*?' she asked, sitting on the edge of the bed and looking searchingly into her face. 'Better than you were?'

Julia knew it was no use pretending with her mother. It was not her health which was being enquired about, it was her happiness.

'I'm better, Mother, truly.'

Helen Barclay smiled. 'Yes, I believe you are—and how much of it is due to Mr Leighton—to Roger?'

Julia frowned a little. 'Mother, just because he brought me home, don't run away with the idea that he—that he and I— He was coming to this part of the country, anyway.'

'Maybe, but he need not have included you in the trip if he hadn't wanted to. You know, I'm glad now that you didn't succeed in buying the boat business yourself. It would have been a big responsibility for you and a great tie, as well as taking all your money. As it is, you're still working with boats, you haven't the responsibility, you can leave any time you like and you still have a little money. And last, but not least, you've met someone else.'

'*Mother!*' remonstrated Julia. 'Because *you've* taken a liking to him, which you obviously have, that doesn't mean there's anything special between him and me. He's merely my boss.'

71

'All right, dear, if you say so. But a person can still be important to you and change your life a great deal without necessarily becoming a permanent part of it. And I think you needed someone like Roger to shift the focus of your thinking away from the past.'

Julia knew what her mother was trying to say. She had needed someone with Roger's strong personality to help her to forget David, though a romantic attachment was not essential. But forget was not the right word. She would never forget David. She had loved him too well.

Watching her face, her mother touched her hand. 'My dear, I know what David meant to you, and a period of grieving—of still reaching out—is natural, but it's all too easy to live in the past, to become obsessed by it.'

Julia smiled faintly and nodded. 'I know.'

Helen Barclay rose and bent to kiss her daughter's cheek. 'Bless you. Good-night, then, and sleep well. It's lovely to have you home again, if only for a short stay.'

Julia put out her light and settled down to sleep, but it did not come easily. Her mind was occupied with so many things. Her mother had so nearly hit on the truth. Roger Leighton had already had some effect on her thinking. She could never feel the same about him as she had about David and there was no question of his ever taking David's place even if he himself had the inclination—which he certainly had not. But there was no denying the fact that for the first time since David's death she had found herself interested in what another man thought of her and was beginning to feel free of the pain which had bound her to David's memory. She thought of Celia Palmer, and became more and more convinced that she and Roger had been in love and had quarrelled. It was obvious that Celia had gone to Norfolk specially to see Roger, and though he might still be angry with her, she was still very much in his mind.

Julia told herself that his private life was nothing to do with her, and plumped up a pillow which had become as hard as a rock, but it was his face and not David's which was etched upon her mental vision as she closed her eyes in sleep.

The week-end passed all too quickly. Shopping with her mother on Saturday morning, lunch in town, and after more shopping in the afternoon, a high tea at home and a theatre in the evening. A lazy day on Sunday with a drive out to the orchards with her father in the afternoon and visiting friends in the evening. It was while she and her father walked for a little while among the still leafless apple trees that her father said:

' If you ever feel you want to come home, you know, Julia, I could do with your help. I've got a new girl in the office, and your work has more or less become split among three other people, including myself, but there are so many things I now have to think about for which you used to take responsibility. Having other people to work for you isn't the same as having your own. And needless to say, I've missed you as a daughter, too. It was pretty good having you around the place, though I realize, of course, that I could never have hoped to keep you at home for ever. Anyway, if you want to come back, don't think for a moment that you'd be doing anyone else out of a job.'

Julia squeezed his hand. ' Thanks, Father. You're the best there is. I might take you up on that. I'll have to see how things work out with Roger Leighton and myself. When the boatyard gets busy I might find I don't like working for him, after all. On the other hand he could very soon tire of the country life and go back to being an oil magnate—or whatever the term is. In which case I presume he'd leave me in charge. At least, I hope he would.'

' And then you'd be happy to stay in Norfolk indefinitely—and possibly marry and settle down there?'

Julia shrugged lightly. ' I expect I shall marry one

73

day, though at the moment—'

'Still can't quite accept the idea of putting anyone in David's place?' her father asked quietly.

'Something like that, I suppose. But I must say, I seem to get more homesick rather than less as time goes on.'

Tom Barclay flashed her a smile. 'They say "home is where your heart is", don't they? See how you feel at the end of the summer. By then you might feel there's nothing to keep you in Norfolk.'

Julia wondered. Perhaps her mother had been right. She had been obsessed by the past which concerned David. Perhaps by the end of the summer she might be glad to leave Norfolk and the boatyard.

On Monday morning Roger called at precisely the hour he said he would, and after a quick cup of coffee to send them on their way, they said goodbye to Julia's parents and set off on their journey back to Norfolk.

After a while, Roger said with insight: 'I hope your week-end didn't unsettle you too much.'

She gave him an amused glance. 'Do you?'

'Of course. I wouldn't like to have to start hunting round for someone to take your place.'

Julia felt rather deflated, but she said swiftly, 'Oh, I wouldn't leave you in the lurch. I'd stay on until at least the end of the season.'

'Does that mean you're thinking of doing so?' he asked sharply.

She laughed briefly. 'Why, no, not necessarily. I mean—simply that, having decided to stay on, if at some time in the future I should change my mind and want to go back home and work for my father, then the end of the season is the time I would choose.'

'I see. But if you had succeeded in buying Wing-craft, you wouldn't even have considered leaving Norfolk, providing the business remained flourishing.'

'I suppose not. But none of us can say with any certainty what we're going to do six months hence, can we?' she countered. 'By the end of the summer you might decide you've had enough yourself.'

'What makes you say that—wishful thinking?'

A swift frown creased her forehead. 'That's—not quite fair, is it?'

The element of truth had found a raw spot, and she was hurt that he should have made the point.

'But it's true, isn't it?' he pressed relentlessly. 'Aren't you rather hoping that I'll get fed up or something like that and leave a clear field for you?'

She felt her cheeks colouring from the unwarranted attack. She would have offered to resign immediately, but she thought he had genuinely meant it when he said he didn't want to start looking for someone to take her place. She could only suppose that he had had a trying week-end. She thought for a moment longer. *Was* she still hoping he would want to sell the business in about six months' time? Honestly, she wasn't, she decided, if only for his sake, because if he did, it would mean that he had failed or had found that he hated the country life. Or even that Celia had persuaded him to go back to the oil company. And that, for some reason, she would find the worst.

'No,' she answered quietly. 'That is *not* what I'm hoping.'

Her answer brought a silence. He took advantage of a red traffic light to turn and look searchingly at her. She met his gaze calmly, but she had the feeling that he was not altogether convinced of her sincerity. He drove in silence for quite a long time, and she did not speak, either. She tried to put her finger on the reason for the small knot of pain deep within her. Was it disappointment that the promising friendly relationship between them was fading, or had already faded? How were they going to work together happily if he did not trust her, if he thought she was waiting for his defeat? It was a very difficult position. She couldn't very well keep changing her mind about staying on even though

75

she was not looking forward to the months ahead. But perhaps he would learn to trust her as time went on, and as soon as the holiday season was in full swing they would be too busy to cut across each other a great deal.

'Would you like another coffee or shall we carry on until lunch-time?' His voice pierced her musings. 'Whichever you feel like will be all right by me.'

Was it her imagination or was there a conciliatory note in his voice? Julia glanced at the car clock which showed a little after eleven.

'Lunch will do fine,' she answered.

'Sure?'

'Quite sure.'

'Then we'll make it an early one. Twelve or there-abouts.' He gave her a sidelong glance. 'Do you like travelling?'

'Motoring, you mean?'

'Yes—and travel in general, seeing places.'

She nodded, glad that he had begun to talk again, and on what should be a fairly safe subject.

'I like motoring—and I must get myself another car. With regard to travel, I'd like to have seen more places than I have.'

'What prevented you—time, money or a suitable travel companion?' he quizzed.

She couldn't help smiling. 'A bit of all three, I suppose. On an annual holiday, one can't see much of the world at a time and the days are gone when parents could afford to send their sons and daughters abroad for six months or a year for their " education ".'

'Only the very wealthy were ever able to do it,' he said. 'And I suppose it's still done today, though money has become more evenly distributed.'

Julia laughed. ' It's the sons and daughters who have the money nowadays—especially if they're in the pop business.' Then she said seriously: 'Actually, my parents would have done more for me if I'd let them, but I'm of the opinion that by the time you're eighteen

76

you should be standing on your own feet.'

'Meaning that what you can't afford yourself you don't have? Very commendable. But suppose you married a rich man?'

Her lips twitched into a smile. 'That would be different, of course, especially if he happened to like travel—foreign or otherwise.'

She thought suddenly how wonderful it would be to travel the world with the right kind of man, one who knew all the ropes, had that air of authority which commanded the best service. A seasoned traveller and a stimulating companion.

'I suppose you've done quite a good deal of travelling?' she said, not realizing the train of her thought.

'Yes, I have, but mostly on business, of course. It's not the same as globe-trotting for pleasure, and travelling alone isn't much fun.'

Julia agreed, then sighed. 'Life is never quite perfect, is it? It always falls short of the ideal.'

'You sound disillusioned. Sometimes people don't recognize the ideal when they have it, or haven't the kind of make-up to appreciate it.'

She denied being disillusioned. 'I was merely thinking that, being engaged in the holiday business as we are, it's rather limiting for foreign travel. I've only just realized that that's one of the things I've long wanted to do. What I mean is, before you misunderstand me, one can't have the best of both worlds. Though there are countries one can visit in the winter, of course.'

But he shook his head. 'It *is* limiting, as you say. And a few weeks' snatched holiday is no way to see the world. If you want to really travel, there's only one thing for it, aside from coming into a fortune. And that's to marry a man who can afford to take you exactly where you want to go and when.'

'Then I shall have to wait a very long time, likely for ever,' she asserted. 'Rich men just don't come

77

my way. Even if one did there'd be no guarantee that he'd want to marry me—or be the travelling kind. There'd also be no guarantee that I'd fall in love with him.'

'So you'd have to be in love with a man before you'd marry him?' he queried.

She gave him a surprised look. 'Now *you're* sounding disillusioned! I'd have to be pretty desperate to marry a man I didn't love, although—'

She broke off, not wanting to continue the train of her thoughts aloud. She was still young enough to want to marry for love, indeed, she could not imagine ever marrying for any other reason. At the same time she could not see herself loving any man in the same way she had loved David.

'You were about to say?' Roger prompted.

She gave an inaudible sigh. This man always demanded an answer!

'This conversation is getting out of hand. All I know is that when you fall in love you don't care whether the person is rich or poor or likes travel or listening to Beethoven. You just *love*—and want, naturally, to spend every minute of the rest of your lives together.'

Her voice trembled. She had not intended saying so much. That was the way David and herself had felt about each other. It had been wonderful, frantic, a feeling beyond the power of words.

There was a short silence. Obviously wanting to pursue the matter, Roger asked in a quiet voice: 'How many times have you been in love, Julia?'

It was on the tip of her tongue to object to such a personal question, but then she began to think. She had had boy-friends before David, of course, and had woven romantic dreams about some of them, but never had she felt the same as she had about him.

'Only once,' she answered Roger briefly.

'And it was love at first sight, I suppose?'

There was no mistaking his sarcasm. 'If you must

know, it was,' she answered tartly, hoping he would take the hint and stop asking personal questions.

He said, after a pause, ' I wouldn't trust that kind of love, myself. I think it's possible to be *attracted* at a first meeting, but that's usually all it is. There's more than one way of falling in love, of course, but I should think it's more a gradual process than a sudden one. I've known couples positively to dislike one another at first, though at no time were they indifferent to each other. They were continually reacting emotionally, either in the way of anger, hurt feelings, shows of pride, but always there was an intense awareness of each other.'

She began to feel amused. ' You sound quite the expert! With all that knowledge of the subject you should never be caught unaware yourself.'

' No, I don't think I would be.'

She wanted to make some sarcastic reply, perhaps to the effect that it was just such clever people who were most likely *to* fall in love without realizing it. But she thought better of it and in a few minutes they came to a likely-looking hotel to have lunch.

Over lunch the conversation turned to travel again, and Roger told her of some of the places he had visited in the course of the family business and would like to see a second time. Julia touched on the few places she had seen and the many more she would like to see.

' Well, if you're going to continue as my second in command, I shall have to see to it that you get adequate holidays at the right time of the year,' he told her.

Julia smiled but said nothing. She couldn't see how that was going to be possible. The popularity of the Broads as a relaxing yet interesting and active holiday grew year by year. Up to a few years ago—when it was thought the Broads had even then reached saturation point—the season was mid-May to mid-September. Now, it was April to October with steady encroachment into March and November. There were foreign coun-

79

tries one could visit in the winter, of course, but those where one could be assured of warm weather were mostly in the Southern Hemisphere and cost a lot of money merely to get there. The Canary Islands on a package tour was about the best she would ever be able to manage.

A sunny week-end and a sudden rise in the general temperature flung away the cloak of winter, galvanized the boat-hire side of the business into action, and Roger Leighton into turning his mind from his house, which was still being decorated, to the business.

'I'm thinking of taking on more men,' he said to Julia one morning.

'Really? With what object?' She had thought the wages bill high enough already, and said so.

But he shook his head. 'If you want to expand you must have more workmen,' he said. 'And I want to increase the fleet to at least twice the number.'

Julia eyed him with consternation. 'To twice the number! But we haven't the facilities.'

'We will have,' he said firmly. 'Meanwhile, now that the yachts and cruisers are all launched there'll be more room in the sheds. And when the need arises I shall have another wet boathouse built, or have the existing one enlarged.'

Julia groaned inwardly. She had liked the business just the size it was.

'What—sort of craft are you going to build? More big cruisers, I suppose?'

He leaned back in the chair behind his own desk and looked up at her. 'Then you'd suppose wrong—but why don't you sit down? I'm sure you can spare a few minutes.'

She sat down and eyed him uncertainly. She might have known he would have ideas for expanding. But why? Why must these business people always think they must expand? She felt it was more important to give an efficient service. She thought of the maintenance which would be required for double the amount of craft, the hectic change-over on Saturday morning when the boats all changed hands and had to be cleaned, and made ready for newcomers, the increase in equipment which would all need taking care of.

'Don't worry,' Roger Leighton said, as if reading her thoughts. 'It will happen so gradually, you'll scarcely notice it. In any case I shan't expect you to do any more work or take any more responsibility than you have at present. To begin with I'm taking on three more men—a yard foreman, a marine maintenance engineer and a boy to take Andy's place. Andy is going to be upgraded. I'm putting him under Frank Willis. He wants to learn boatbuilding.'

'That sounds like a good idea—but why do we want a yard foreman?' It sounded ominously like the thin end of a wedge. She had virtually shared this role with Frank.

'Because I don't want Frank to be continually leaving his job to help in general boatyard duties. I've told you—I'm stepping up production. In time, of course, you'll need a girl to help you in the office. Now, any questions?' he asked with a hint of mockery.

'You haven't told me yet what kind of craft you're having built,' she pointed out.

'Oh, didn't I? Auxiliary yachts, mostly—with cruiser comfort and all mod. cons. such as sprung cabin tops, a winch for raising and lowering the mast and roller reefing.'

Julia's eyes gleamed. 'Have you had them designed yet?'

'Not yet. I thought you might have some ideas. I thought two, three and four berths. And I've got an idea for some new-type half-deckers for day hire.'

'Tell me more,' she invited.

'Well, in my opinion, if more thought is not given to the vagaries of our weather when designing sailing craft, sailing might well disappear from the Broads

81

altogether, and that would be a pity. So I'm going to have a prototype half-deckers made with a small cabin —not big enough to sleep in, but just big enough for two people to take shelter when there are sudden sharp showers or thunderstorms.'

Julia smiled broadly. He was a man after her own heart. He was not just a money-making executive, after all.

'I take it you approve?' he prompted.

'I certainly do. There are a *few* half-deckers on the Broads with what's called "stowage shelter" for'ard, but they're precious little use when the rain drives in. But why not, as a quick job, get Frank to convert the two we have? There's plenty of deck space for'ard— more really than is necessary. A top and sides could be built on and still leave a large well for manoeuvring. He could do one at a time.'

'Right,' he said promptly. 'I'll speak to him about it.'

The telephone on his desk rang and he lifted the receiver. She saw him frown, then he looked at her. 'It's for you—Max Windham.'

'I'll take it in my office.'

She rose and went through. It was some weeks since she had either seen or heard anything from Max. Not since the night he had asked her out to dinner and she had gone with Roger. She lifted the receiver and heard Roger replace his.

'Hello, Max.'

'Ah, Julia. Thought I'd better make contact again —find out how things are going. Long time, no see.'

She winced at the cliché. 'Well, I daresay we've both been busy. How are you?'

'Been missing you. But I—er—got the idea you were giving me the brush-off, seeing with with Leighton in town after you'd said you were having an early night.'

'I'm sorry about that,' she told him. 'He asked me, and I didn't feel I could refuse.'

82

He gave a noncommittal grunt. 'I take it we're still friends, then?'

'Of course.' She could scarcely say otherwise.

'Well, look—it's the boat sale tomorrow and I'll be tied up. The same Friday and over the week-end.'

'The girl I saw you with at the hotel that night?' she quizzed.

'No. Actually, I'm off to London on some business of my father's. But what about next Monday? We could catch up on what news there is over a bite to eat.'

After a momentary hesitation, she agreed. After all, she had nothing against Max, and an evening out now and then was something she enjoyed. Max said he would call for her, then they said goodbye and rang off. A few minutes later Roger came through.

'I thought you'd finished with that young man,' he remarked.

She looked at him in astonishment, then found annoyance and amusement fighting for supremacy. She dealt swiftly with all three and answered coolly:

'Now, why should you think that?'

'I've told you. He isn't your type. You're just wasting your time,' he flung out as he walked to the door.

Julia gave up. 'By the way, it's the spring boat sale at Wroxham tomorrow. You might find it interesting. They're held twice a year, spring and autumn.'

He turned. 'Now you mention it, I did see it advertised. Have we anything in ourselves?'

She shook her head. 'Not this year. Occasionally we put a boat in. At least, according to the records.'

'Would you like to go?' he asked.

'Er—yes, I wouldn't mind.'

'Right, then we'll both go and have some lunch down there together—unless you've already made a date with your friend Windham.'

These references to Max were not really funny. What

had he against him? she wondered. She looked at Roger squarely.

' I try to keep my private life separate from my working life,' she told him. ' I would certainly not have arranged to be out on a working day without consulting you first.'

His face darkened. ' I don't want you to account for every move,' he answered. ' And I didn't mean to interfere with your private life.'

He went out and Julia stared after him. He was a puzzle to her at times, and she was never quite sure how to take him. She supposed if she were one of his secretaries, the kind he had been used to in the oil business, she would know the exact relationship required and attitude to adopt. She would simply have to try a little harder.

The weather the following day was typical for April and fairly typical for the Wroxham boat sale—showery, and warm when the sun came out. There had also been plenty of rain during the night, and knowing from experience what conditions would be like underfoot Julia donned Wellington boots, tucking in the legs of her navy slacks. Under her suede jacket she wore a white polo-necked sweater and tied a waterproof scarf over her hair.

' I see you're prepared for the worst,' Roger remarked as she took her seat beside him in his car.

It was the nearest to a compliment she was likely to get, Julia thought, though she knew the white sweater looked well and suited her. She made some bantering reply and felt suddenly stimulated as she often did in his company.

The stretch of ground which was littered with lots under the ' miscellaneous ' heading was a series of yellow pools, but as usual the variety of bits and pieces awaiting the auctioneer's hammer was fascinating. Items ranged from the wierdest of home-made fend-offs to boat trailers, and in between, everything one could think of which might possibly be of some use in, on, or around a boat. Weights and round anchors of all sizes, disconsolate lengths of mooring rope, new and second-hand, port and starboard lights, old cooking stoves, several pairs of oars, one or two bunk mattresses, and absurdly, things like a drunken, bursting leather armchair, and an old desk, and some objects which were simply unidentifiable, being parts of some whole, for which someone might find a remote use.

Roger stared at some of the things. ' Does anyone really buy this junk?' he asked in astonishment.

' Somebody will find a use for it, I daresay,' she answered. ' And it isn't *all* junk.'

They stopped now and then to listen to the auctioneer as he rattled off his patter from the top of a step-ladder, and here and there saw a man bear off some item in triumph which he had managed to wrestle from an opponent in the bidding.

They squelched through the mud, skirting still larger yellow pools, to look at the small craft waiting to be auctioned. There were racing dinghies, rowing boats, motor launches, canoes, and the occasional catamaran, their owners keeping guard while prospective buyers peered and prodded and assessed the possible price.

Last of all to be auctioned were usually the bigger craft jostling each other for mooring space at an allocated quayside.

' I'd like to know how much some of these fetch,' murmured Roger.

Julia glanced at her catalogue. ' To be auctioned at half past two. We've got time to have lunch first.'

They had lunch at a restaurant overlooking the river, and Julia was reminded of the last time she and David had been here.

' Penny for them,' offered Roger.

She shook her head, smiling. ' They're worth a little more than that,' she answered. But the memory of David no longer hurt her or made her feel lonely.

85

All around them were people talking about boats. Wroxham had a special atmosphere on days such as this. The sun came out, and they sat outside after lunch to drink their coffee, then joined the crowds of people as the various craft were auctioned—always something of a gamble. There were several half-deckers, some ex-Broads hire-craft—auxiliary yachts as well as cruisers, a number of houseboats, speedboats, and various kinds of launches. There was also a luxury six-berth cruiser beautifully ' furnished.'

' Would you like one like that?' asked Roger.

' To own, you mean—for my private use?'

' Yes.'

Julia laughed. ' Chance would be a fine thing! I suppose a little bit of luxury is nice now and then, and I don't see why one should necessarily be uncomfortable on a boat. But seriously I'd much prefer to own either a half-decker or an auxiliary. Yes, I think that would be the height of my ambition. To own a two-berth auxiliary with all the mod. cons. like you're planning, plus a few additions of my own.'

' Such as? That's something we haven't gone into, isn't it?'

' Better weather protection for one thing so that you can cruise in all conditions without getting either wet or frozen to death, and for another, real cabin comfort such as upholstered backrests on the settee-berths, plenty of shelf-space, handy hooks for jackets as well as cupboard space.'

' A Wingcraft Special,' commented Roger.

Occasionally Julia searched the crowds for a sight of Max, but did not see him even among those clustered around the auctioneer during the sale of the larger craft in which he usually displayed great keenness.

' Quite an interesting day,' Roger said when there remained only a few houseboats to auction. ' But it's getting chilly now. How about something more to eat?'

And so they finished the day in one of the locals which

served cold meats and salads and cheese and biscuits, and they became part of a group of people who had also been to the sale, discussing sales past and present, comparing prices and generally yarning about boats. Julia thought that, contrary to Max's prophecy, Roger was settling down to life on Broadland very well indeed.

On Saturday afternoon Julia had occasion to go into town. She did some shopping and finished her various errands, then dropped into a hotel for a cup of tea. She was passing the door of the lounge when she suddenly halted at the sight of two people sitting at the farthest end. For a moment she just stood and stared, scarcely able to believe her eyes.

It was Max, and with him was Celia Palmer.

CHAPTER FIVE

Julia was telling herself that it couldn't be Max, he
was in London, but suddenly he looked up and saw her.
She turned away swiftly and, changing her mind about
having tea there, crossed the foyer to the outer doors.
But she had no sooner stepped on to the pavement when
he caught up with her.

'Julia, wait a minute!'

She looked at him coldly. 'So you changed your
mind about going to London?' She had a strong suspicion that he had never had any intention of going.
She knew him well enough to know that he had no
conscience about lying to get himself out of a difficulty.

'It was Father who changed *his* mind,' he told her
quickly. 'He decided to go himself. I was going to
ring you. Then I came in here and met Celia—'

Celia. Julia's eyes widened. 'And how long have
you known Miss Palmer?'

He took a deep breath. 'Look, Julia, I'll explain
everything to you when I see you on Monday. Right
now I want to ask you not to mention to Leighton that
you've seen Celia. She doesn't want him to know she's
here. What I mean is, she wants to surprise him, to—to
tell him herself. I understand he has rather a jealous
disposition too, so if you don't mind—'

'Don't worry, Max. I wouldn't dream of telling him
that I saw you together.'

Relief showed in his face. 'Good. See you on Monday, then, as arranged?'

'Yes, all right.'

She left him and he went back into the hotel. She
wasn't at all anxious to see him on Monday, but at least
she would hear his explanation about Celia. She was
reasonably sure that Roger had no idea the two knew
each other at all, and she was happy that he was being

deceived. She could well imagine that Roger could be a jealous man. Was that why Celia and he had quarrelled?

Julia was no uneasy about the situation she did not bother about having tea after all. She drove straight back to the boatyard. She saw no sign of Roger, and his car was not standing outside the house as it so often was during the day. It was usually only last thing at night when he had finally finished with it that he ran it into the garage. The boatyard was deserted, the workmen having gone home and the few cruisers on hire had left their moorings for the week. It was too early in the year and too chilly for day boats to be hired, and Julia let herself into the houseboat feeling incredibly lonely.

But about eight o'clock, just as it was growing dark, there came a knock on the door and she opened it to see Roger there. For a moment she felt guilty and wondered whether Celia had let him know yet that she was in the area. She really hated not being able to tell him and felt most disloyal.

'I was wondering whether you'd like to come and play the piano for a while and have a drink with me,' he said. 'That is, if you're not going out.'

She experienced a small thrill of pleasure which was short-lived as she realized that Celia could not have contacted him.

'No, I'm not going out,' she told him. 'Shall I come now, or—' She glanced down at her dress, thinking she would like to change into something a little better.

But he said: 'Yes, come now. You don't need to change on my acount. You look very well as you are— and the place is hardly the height of luxury yet.'

She slipped a coat across her shoulders and they walked across to the house together.

'I thought if it's a fine day tomorrow we might take one of the half-deckers out,' he said. 'Always with the proviso that you're not otherwise engaged.'

'The same goes for you,' she answered. 'And on that understanding, it's a date.'

'There's not much chance of my being "otherwise engaged",' he said. 'But—Max Windham apart—I can't understand why you should be alone on a Saturday evening. Or any other evening. You ought to get out more—make some new friends.'

His tone was almost accusing. She could not understand quite what he was driving at, and neither did she know exactly how to answer him. But she thought she ought to make some effort.

'The boatyard keeps me pretty busy—and I've never been in the habit of going out on Saturday evenings in particular.'

'Maybe not. I haven't myself, but you're practically married to this boatyard, and it isn't right.'

She looked at him in surprise. 'If I'm happy, I don't see why anyone else should worry.'

He had nothing to say to that. They reached the house and he ushered her inside. By now, work on the structural alterations had been completed. Part of the wall separating lounge and dining room was gone and a most pleasing arch had been fashioned at each side where the division had been, giving rather a 'classic' appearance to the room.

'The heating engineers are coming in on Monday,' he told her. 'And when they've finished, the decorators will start.'

'Will you just have this part done?' she asked.

He shook his head. 'The whole house. Perhaps you'd take a look around before you go and give me your opinion about colour schemes.'

'Yes, of course, but you mentioned the possibility of getting married. Oughtn't your future wife to be consulted?'

He nodded. 'She will be. Will you have a glass of sherry?'

The evening passed very pleasantly. While they were

having a drink he brought out some auxiliary yacht designs to show her, and she told him her ideas for either a forward drive or a well cover with a window so positioned that the user could be under cover when the yacht was being used as a cruiser. They had a most lively discussion, but at the end of it he approved her idea.

'I'll have a consultation with Frank Willis, then get a design drawn.'

After this they went upstairs where there were three moderately sized double bedrooms and a fourth which would be equally suitable either as a single room or a boxroom.

'What would *you* do with it?' he asked her.

'It's hard to say. It depends on how much entertaining you intend doing. You'll probably be a fair target for those relatives who want a holiday in this area.'

'Never mind about me. Suppose it were your house —how would you use it?' he insisted.

'Well, as you've got the other three rooms, I'd just redecorate this small one and leave it empty, see what the need turns out to be later. I'm no great believer in storing junk anyway. It could be used as a sewing room, a hobbies room, a —'

'A nursery?' he prompted, his lips curving into a smile.

She nodded and smiled back at him. 'Exactly.'

They went from room to room. One bedroom was bigger than the other two. Julia suggested that there was enough space for a private bathroom and twin wash-basins.

'A sort of "his and hers"? Good idea.'

Julia had a sudden vision of him sharing this room with Celia and her mind boggled at the idea somehow. She suggested a colour scheme and was glad to move on to the other rooms.

When they went downstairs again he insisted on Julia playing the piano while he went into the kitchen and made coffee. He had had the piano tuned, and it sounded good. She couldn't help envying Celia—if it really was she whom he was going to marry. The houseboat was very nice and comfortable enough in its way, but it would be lovely to live in a house again, to have a piano one could just sit down and play at any time. There was one at home, of course. She began to realize how much she had missed music.

'You play well,' Roger remarked when he brought in a tray laden with coffee, sandwiches, cheese and biscuits.

She swung round on the stool. 'Not as well as I'd like to. I'm out of practice.'

'You must remedy that when the men have finished the work.'

But she felt sure he was only being polite. 'Does Celia play?' she asked, without thinking.

'Celia?' he repeated in a puzzled voice. 'I don't really know. I don't think so.'

The query didn't seem to have pleased him, and she wished she had not made it.

She eyed the tray and said, to cover up: 'You've been busy. I wouldn't have thought you were so domesticated.'

He smiled. 'Nothing to it. Ready sliced bread and ham—cheese and biscuits cook themselves, and Mrs Harris does the shopping.'

Picture of a bachelor. It didn't seem right at all. 'Anything I can do, any time,' she offered.

But he shook his head swiftly. 'Mrs Harris does it as part of her job. It *isn't* a part of yours. Now—black or white?' he added before she could answer him.

She felt a little hurt and snubbed at his turning down her offer so unequivocally. He was a man whom it was difficult to understand at times.

She thought so even more the following day. It was fine and sunny with enough breeze to make the anticipation of some sailing—and with Roger—very, very pleasant indeed. No time had been mentioned, so as it was Sunday, Julia lingered over her morning tea, had a leisurely bath and a prolonged breakfast of bacon and egg and toast. She had a feeling that Roger Leighton would be the kind of man who liked a leisurely Sunday morning too, though for her part these would be curtailed as summer drew near and people wanted to take out boats for the day. When she had washed up and tidied the houseboat, she wandered outside hoping Roger would be somewhere around. But he was nowhere to be seen. Should she take the cover off the boat and get her ready for pushing off or would he prefer to do that himself? There were two half-deckers, Winglet 1 and 2. Twin craft. Julia chose the one in the best position for getting out and began to unhook the awning. He couldn't possibly object to her doing that. And after that, surely there would be no harm in going to knock on his door.

She took her time in removing the boat cover and folded it up neatly, then went round to the house. She raised her hand to knock, then halted. She could hear voices within. She listened for a moment, then unmistakably came a woman's voice. Celia's.

Slowly, Julia turned away. She might have known! There would be no sailing with Roger today. She went back to the boat, picturing Celia looking over the rooms, discussing colour schemes. How different would Celia's choice be from her own? It was ridiculous of Roger to ask her opinion last night. It was too late even to change that of the living/dining room.

Julia unfastened the ties of the sail thinking to herself that as soon as the man arrived who was on Sunday duty she would cast off. Though it was sunny, it was unlikely that they would have any customers for day boat hire. The cool wind would put most people off.

She was hoisting sail when Roger and Celia appeared. Celia looked distinctly uncomfortable, screwing up her face against the wind and holding a protective hand on her hair. Roger walked up to Julia and eyed the sail.

' I see you're ready for the off,' he said.

' Yes. It would be a pity to waste the day,' she answered without looking at him.

' I have to run Celia back to town—'

' That's all right. We made the proviso last night, remember?'

Celia had wandered across to an eight-berth cruiser, one of their luxury craft. She called out to Roger. Julia saw him hesitate, and pride came to her aid.

' Don't feel under any obligation to me,' she told him. ' I can handle this boat perfectly well on my own, and in one minute from now I shall be pushing off.'

' Roger, do come and show me how to get inside this lovely-looking boat—!' came Celia's voice.

Julia winced at the phrase as Roger strode over to the large cruiser. The next minute she had cast off, navigating carefully past the other moored craft. She felt more ragged and disappointed than she ought to be or had any right to be, and how she longed once again for David. She turned into the open river with the wind right behind her. She would have to tack most of the way back, but she didn't care.

Before very long, however, owing to the keen air and physical exercise, hunger overtook her. This was a quiet part of the river and she knew there was nowhere for miles where one could get a meal—and she had come out without money in any case. There was nothing for it but to turn the yacht into the wind and begin the zig-zag course from one side to the other to fill out the sail, though she would have liked to stay out for much longer.

Fortuntely, the wind stayed brisk and veered a little so that at times she was able to take longish tacks and gain a boat or so's length on the turn. All the same, she was so hungry by the time she reached the boatyard, she called out to Charlie, the workman, to moor her and ease off the sail. Tea and sandwiches were the quickest thing, she decided, and was chewing away

94

standing up when a knock came at the door. Thinking it would be Charlie, she went to answer it, a sandwich in her hand. It was Roger. She swallowed hastily and gestured to come in.

'Is this your Sunday lunch?' he enquired, as he eyed the bread and butter and cold meat on the table.

She nodded. 'I was so hungry I couldn't wait to prepare anything else.'

'Sorry this morning misfired,' he said. 'I had planned to sail up to Sutton and take you to lunch there.'

'I'm sorry, too.' Perhaps if she had waited for a little while instead of being in such a hurry— 'What happened to Celia?' she asked.

'She had to go back to London. I gave her lunch first, then saw her on to the train.'

'When did she come down?' Julia couldn't resist the question.

'Late last night, I gather.'

Late last night. Why bother to lie? Was Roger really as jealous as all that? Celia couldn't even have mentioned Max.

'You know, you shouldn't be having a snack lunch like this,' Roger told her. 'You need proper meals.'

She assured him she would have a sort of high tea later, wondering whether he was genuinely concerned or extending his role as managing director. As he made no effort to leave, she asked him if he'd like a cup of tea with her, but he shook his head.

'Seeing that you had come back, I came to ask if it was too late for our sail. Perhaps you'd rather not go out again. The wind *is* rather cold.'

She laughed, feeling light-hearted again. 'It's nothing to a hardened yachtsman like me. I'd love another run. I came back because I was hungry.'

He left her to finish her sandwiches in peace, and a quarter of an hour later they pushed off. Julia guessed that really he was anxious to test her sailing prowess.

For her part, she was certainly curious about this, and later was secretly surprised at his skill both when running before the wind and tacking. He had some words of praise for her skill, too.

'You can certainly handle a boat,' he said. 'Do you do dinghy sailing—racing and all that?'

But she shook her head. 'I like this kind best. Oddly enough I'm not in love with just sailing on one of the Broads, I prefer this kind—getting from A to B, as it were.'

He nodded in agreement. 'There's more to sailing these rivers than many people imagine. There are so many twists and turns. You need a different set of the sail around every bend. I find it a challenge.'

Julia smiled. 'Pitting your wits against the elements is always a challenge.' She wondered if Celia cared for sailing, or had even set foot inside a boat.

'By the way, what did Celia think of *Wing of the Morning*?' she asked when a stretch of river made running free possible.

He glanced up at the burgee fluttering in the wind. 'She thought it very smart, of course. And I'm afraid something like that is more in her line than a yacht. She wants to come down for a holiday, but we're fully booked from about next week-end onward, aren't we?'

Julia received this news with anything but delight, somehow. 'Just about. I'd have to look at the books. It would depend on what she wants and when she wants it,' she answered without enthusiasm.

'As she would be coming alone, I think a houseboat with a launch would meet her requirements. She had a look at one or two of them and thought them very smart and comfortable.'

'I very much doubt if there's a houseboat unbooked during the main holiday season,' she told him—'though of course, it does sometimes happen that there's a cancellation at the last minute.'

She couldn't help feeling that she ought to offer

accommodation to Celia in her own houseboat, but she baulked at the idea. Why, she wasn't sure. She was not normally inhospitable, and she could hardly say she disliked Celia. She did not knew her well enough except that she felt deceiving Roger about her arrival in Norwich and her friendship with Max was not very good. But whatever the reason, the thought of Celia staying for weeks in one the houseboats, strolling around the boatyard, going in and out of Roger's office and spending time in the house depressed her utterly.

About an hour later they brought the half-decker in to moor again and went through the business of making the boat secure, furling the sail and fastening on the cover for the night. This done, Roger thanked her for coming, said goodnight and strode away without lingering in the least, leaving Julia haunted with the thought that he was probably displeased because she *hadn't* offered hospitality to Celia.

Loneliness settled even more heavily upon her as she prepared her solitary evening meal, read a book and watched a little television. It was a truism, she thought when she put out her light to go to sleep, that man was not meant to live alone. During the summer when there was plenty of activity even until quite late, it was not so bad, but she really would have to do something about her present state at the end of the season, find someone with whom to share a flat, perhaps. She thought of Roger alone in his house. But undoubtedly he would not be alone for such longer. Then Celia would be in and around the boatyard and coming and going day after day, week after week, year after year. Julia turned restlessly. In that event she did not think she would stay a moment longer than she had to.

Reluctantly, the next day, Julia examined the bookings of the houseboats and did not know whether she felt relieved or not that they were all booked up.

'I could try some of the other boatyards,' she suggested to Roger.

As she expected, he shook his head. 'I'm quite sure she wouldn't like that.'

Julia was sure, too. There was no help for it. She said the only thing she felt she possibly *could* say. 'She could—share my houseboat for a week or two if—' She broke off. From his expression it was difficult to say whether the idea pleased him or not. Certainly he was not smiling.

'That's very noble of you,' he said. 'But it's up to you, of course. Don't feel under an obligation of any kind.'

He passed through to his own office and she gazed after him uncertainly. One might almost think he was offended. She sighed raggedly and continued with her work.

Max called for her that evening as arranged, and as she stepped into his car, Roger came out of the house. He looked extremely displeased about something, but Julia thought there was often no accounting for Roger's pleasures or displeasures.

'You look as though you might be finding life rather difficult,' Max remarked, glancing at her face as they drove away.

'Not really,' she answered briefly.

'All the same, I shouldn't think Leighton is a very easy man to get along with. At least, from what Celia tells me.'

'I don't think she ought to talk about him like that. In fact, I find it rather despicable.'

'Well, she only *hinted*. It doesn't take much knowledge of him to be able to put two and two together. I more or less drew her out. I could sense that she wanted to talk—to confide in someone, so to speak.'

'I didn't even know you had met each other,' Julia said. 'When did you?'

'A few weeks ago, actually. She was staying in Norwich, and we shared a table at lunch at the hotel. Hers was the only table with a vacant place. Naturally, we got talking, then after lunch I asked her if she'd like to see round our place. She was very impressed, I can tell you.'

Max went on talking and Julia had the impression that he was saying anything and everything that came into his head. But she was only half listening, in any case. She was thinking how odd it was that Max and Celia should have so quickly become friendly, and how disloyal Celia was to Roger. She could not forget the photograph which had dropped on to the study floor, or of the absent-minded way Roger had drawn her face. Surely he must still be in love with her—also she with him. Why else should she be making these visits to Norfolk? On the other hand, why should she have been meeting Max? She would not have thought it necessary to be trying to make Roger jealous. A great deal of what was happening did not make sense.

For a meal they went to one of the country clubs which abounded in Norfolk, especially in the Broads area, and when they had given their order, Max leaned across the table and gave her a long, enquiring look.

' Well now, my lovely, tell me honestly, how are you finding life with the man in possession, and what's happening at Wingcraft? Do you really see any chance of his getting fed up and leaving the field clear for you?'

Julia met his gaze and took a deep breath and shook her head.

' You can't seriously expect me to give you clear-cut answers to questions like that?'

He smiled persuasively. ' You can try. For instance, how is Leighton treating you? I wouldn't say you're looking too happy.'

Julia frowned. This was the most difficult question of all to answer. Truthfully, she did not know it herself. She could only touch on the surface.

' He's treating me as a colleague,' she said. ' In fact we had quite an interesting discussion only the other

99

evening about a new design for an auxiliary.'

Max's expression alerted. 'Oh? With what special features?'

But Julia smiled knowingly. 'You don't expect me to tell you, do you?'

He grinned. 'No harm in trying. Anyway, you could trust me, couldn't you?'

'No,' she told him frankly.

He laughed. 'Whose design was it, anyway? Not his, I shouldn't think. If it was, I'm sure it wouldn't be any good.'

'That's not fair. How do you know what gifts or knowledge he has?' she said defensively. 'Anyway, as it happens, it was mine. And he's going to use it.'

'Oh? Having new auxiliaries built, is he?'

'Yes, he is, I'm pleased to say. More half-deckers, too.'

Max gave a grunt of derision. 'That shows what a poor hand he is at our business. Sailing is on the way out. People want the comfort and luxury of today's cruisers. Sailing's too much like hard work. Most people work hard enough for fifty weeks of the year. They want a rest when they go on holiday. Besides, our weather's so unreliable.'

'Exactly, and our new auxiliaries are being designed with that very factor in mind.'

He shrugged. 'Well, that's the way to lose money.'

'I'm glad he isn't all that mercenary. It's possible to give a service as well as make money—which is what most business people seem to forget nowadays.'

'I doubt if putting more sailing craft on the Broads is giving people what they want. In fact, I'm sure it's *not*. I expect Leighton is one of those people with heads full of useless ideals. He thinks sails look pretty and *he* would like to see more sail craft just for the pleasure of seeing them go up and down the river. But why try to foist your own ideals and ideas on to other people?'

'Sailing craft not only look well on the rivers and

Broads, they're also quieter,' Julia reminded him. 'And they don't do nearly so much damage to the river banks.'

'*That* I would dispute, too,' said Max. 'But why should I worry? I for one wouldn't be sorry to see him high-tail it back to where he came from, and I would have thought that would suit you, as well.' He eyed her keenly. 'But you seem to have lost the ambition you once had for being the owner of Wingcraft—unless—' He broke off.

'Unless what?' Julia prompted quietly.

He grinned rather sheepishly. 'You're not the type, of course. But one way of owning the business—or being part-owner, at any rate—would be to marry him.'

Julia drew an angry breath. 'If you mean I'm not the type to marry for those sort of reasons, you're so right. You're right about my ambition, too, I think. It doesn't seem nearly so imperative that I should own Wingcraft.' Her anger subsided. 'But enough about our boatyard. What about yours? All ready for the season?'

'Oh, yes,' he answered a little gloomily. 'The first batch of happy holiday-makers went off on Saturday, and next Saturday we have a dozen or more ditto. How I hate Saturday mornings. The stuff some of the clients bring with them—and mostly just for a week—is fantastic. Transistors, guitars, packages and parcels containing heaven knows what, whacking great suitcases—'

'Why not? It's their holiday,' Julia pointed out. 'It's you who'd be the poorer if they didn't come.'

He gave a grunt of derision. 'Maybe, maybe not. I've told you before what it's like being the boss's son. You're just a dogsbody around the place.'

'Oh, Max, you're exaggerating,' she protested, though she had known for some time that he found it irksome working for his father.

'Am I?'

There was a note of bitterness in his voice she had

never heard until now. But before she could either frame words of sympathy or suggest he did something about it, his mood changed.

He smiled and gave a shrug. 'I'm sorry. I *am* being a wet blanket, aren't I?' He broke off as a waiter approached. 'Ah, here comes the food. Let's eat, drink and be merry, as the saying goes.'

He waited until they had been served and were eating before saying:

'So Leighton does have ideas of expanding?'

She nodded. 'A man like him would hardly be content to stand still.'

'No,' he agreed. 'But I wouldn't have thought he'd go in for something that wasn't going to bring him sure returns. Is he going to take on more hands, build more sheds—things like that? He'll need to.'

Julia hesitated, reluctant to discuss her employer's plans, and yet there was nothing really secret in the fact of a firm expanding their business.

She compromised. 'He has quite a number of long-term plans, but his only immediate ones are to take on one or two more men and start building more craft.'

'What sort of men is he taking on? Another boat-builder?' queried Max.

She shook her head. 'No, Frank Willis will be carrying on with the boat-building side, and Roger—'

'Roger?' interposed Max, his eyes widening suddenly. 'So you're on Christian name terms now, are you?'

She looked at him in surprise. 'Why not? It's easier, isn't it—when you're working with anyone.'

'Even when one happens to be the boss?'

'It was his suggestion. In any case—'

He gave an apologetic smile. 'I'm sorry. I was a bit surprised, that's all. But I interrupted you. You were about to say?'

She had almost lost her trend of thought. 'Well, he talked of a marine engineer and a yard foreman so that

Frank could work on the boat-building without so many interruptions.'

Max grimaced. 'He means business, apparently. But I would have thought *you* were capable of looking after the boatyard. You and old Hargreaves managed between you last season. What's Leighton—I beg your pardon—Roger going to do? Sit in his office all day or just walk around with his hands in his pockets?'

Julia carefully controlled a rising anger. Never again would she come out for an evening with Max. She could not stand his continual criticisms of Roger Leighton.

'He is the boss,' she pointed out tepidly. 'He is entitled to do as he pleases, I imagine. Time alone will tell, of course, but he doesn't strike me as being the kind who will be content to do either of the things you mention.'

Max took a sip of his wine. 'You're always very ready to spring to his defence these days. How do you know that bringing in a foreman isn't the thin end of the wedge as far as you're concerned? The next thing will be a manager. He's just using you at the moment because you know the business. As soon as he begins to feel his feet you'll be relegated to the role of office girl, and if you try managing things he'll get rid of you.'

Julia put down her knife and fork. Max had so nearly expressed her own half-formed fears it was more than she could take.

'Max, do you mind if we talk about something else other than the boatyard? It's all so much useless speculation anyway. I shall stay on at Wingcraft just for as long as I'm reasonably happy and contented. In any case, I shall think very seriously of going back home at the end of the season.'

'The very fact of your talking in those terms is an indication that you're not happy,' insisted Max.

The sweets trolley was brought to them, and Julia chose with little interest. She did not know whether she was happy or not. What was happiness? She had been happy at home, she decided, and she had been deliriously happy knowing David. Now—

She ate the last spoonful of her sweet without tasting it, and as soon as they had had their coffee she said she'd like to go home. Max raised his eyebrows and shot a look of enquiry at her, but said nothing. Julia felt miserable without knowing why, and this fact made her feel all the more ragged.

When Max stopped the car near the houseboat, he switched off the headlights and engine and turned to her, resting his arm on the back of the seat.

'Well, here you are, Julia. Thanks for an enjoyable evening.'

At this she felt conscience-stricken. 'I've cut it a little short, I'm afraid. I'm sorry.'

'That's all right. But—as a matter of interest—was I boring you or something?'

'Of course not.'

'In that case there's only one other thing for it. I annoyed you by saying things about Leighton.'

She sighed, 'Oh, Max, please don't start again!'

His arm slid across her shoulders. 'You know *why* I don't like the man, don't you?'

She moved restlessly. 'Well, no, I don't. He hasn't done you any harm.'

'Maybe not—yet. But he did snatch Wingcraft from *you*, didn't he? Apart from that, I'm jealous of him.'

She looked at him in amazement. 'Jealous of him? What on earth do you mean?'

'He sees more of you than I do for one thing. And for another, I have the feeling that you're becoming rather smitten with him.'

Julia felt a sharp stab of something like pain. But she rejected Max's suggestion swiftly.

'Really, Max, you are being silly tonight. If I've defended him it's been out of no other motive than ordinary loyalty. *And* fairness.'

'All right,' he said in a resigned voice.

He leaned towards her with the obvious intention of kissing her, but Julia shrank from the idea and pushed him away.

'No, please, Max. I—just don't feel like it. I'm sorry. Thanks very much for the dinner. It was a lovely meal, but I'll say goodnight now if you don't mind.'

He removed his arm without a word and reached out for the ignition. It was easy to see she had annoyed him, which wasn't really surprising. But Julia felt it would be useless to offer further apology. She opened the car door and stepped out.

'Goodnight, Max—'

His reply was scarcely audible. Before she had time to insert her key in the lock of the houseboat he had started up the engine and reversed out of the boatyard.

Julia sighed deeply. How complicated life was! Or seemed. Strictly speaking she *ought* to be more happy and more contented than she was. The overwhelming grief she had known with David's death had passed. It had had to. One simply does not go on grieving deeply for ever, even for one's very nearest and dearest. One has to learn to live, even though one never forgets. She would always have a special place in her heart for David. No, it was not because of David's death that she felt restless and at odds with life, that things worried or irritated her which usually would not.

She made a drink and slipped into a housecoat and lay on top of her bed thinking, trying to sort herself out. Perhaps this disturbance of her normally balanced behaviour and outlook on life stemmed from her disappointment with regard to the buying of Wingcraft. She had wanted it so much, she had had so many plans. Her mind went back. Why had she wanted it so badly? Pride of ownership, a desire to be her own boss? But more than these things at the time, she had wanted it for David's sake, partly because she thought *he* would want her to have it and partly because she could not bear the thought of anyone taking David's place. It would sound silly and sentimental to some people, she supposed. And in retrospect, it didn't make a great deal of sense to herself. She didn't mind seeing Roger about the place. She felt sure David wouldn't have, either.

She allowed her mind to dwell on Roger and it dawned upon her that she liked him a very great deal. Yet why was she so constantly stirred up? He was treating her as a colleague, she made as many decisions and worked with the same freedom as she had when Mr Hargreaves had been alive, and Roger was even putting some of her own plans into operation. She should be happy. All the ingredients were there. All, that was, except— She baulked at the idea that she was not fully happy just because she wanted love and marriage. Only a bare half hour ago, she had repulsed Max. She had liked him well enough until he had begun to criticize Roger so much.

The more she thought of Roger the more she realized what a man after her own heart he was. He was different from David, a more complex character. But he was the kind of man with whom she would go anywhere, venture anything. She would never want to leave him.

Suddenly Julia knew without any shadow of doubt that she was in love with Roger.

CHAPTER VI

Julia quickly discovered that loving Roger was totally different from the way she had been in love with David. Between David and herself it had been mutual. There had been no pretence, no shyness or misunderstandings, no complications, no other girl. No Celia. She did not even love Roger in the same way. This was a quieter love. At least, for the time being. And more deep. She was like a person who has been given a rare and precious gift. It was not something to shout about, to make public. It was something to cherish. It gave her an undefinable sense of peace, a quietness of spirit. That Roger did not love her seemed not to matter at this stage. She simply accepted the existence of Celia without dwelling too much on the future.

Roger glanced up from his desk one morning when she took in some letters for him to sign and gave her a long, enquiring look.

'Is anything—wrong, Julia? At least, not wrong, exactly, but—'

She placed the letters before him. 'Nothing is wrong—why?'

'I don't know. But you seem different.'

She smiled faintly. She *was* different. 'Perhaps it's the rise in the temperature,' she told him. Then, on a sudden impulse and because she wanted to please him, she said: 'By the way, I was wondering if you'd like me to write to Celia—to Miss Palmer—and offer her accommodation in the houseboat My houseboat, I mean, of course. After all, if I wasn't using it, we—you—could be letting it. And it ought really to be earning money. It's intended for four anyway. Celia could have my cabin and I could sleep on the studio couch. That way I wouldn't disturb her in the mornings.' As she spoke she knew in her bones she was making a great mistake, but it was out now and could not be unsaid.

He did not answer for a moment. He kept his gaze fixed upon her as if trying to read some ulterior motive into what she had said. Then he drew an audible breath as though giving up. He searched among the papers on his desk.

'As a matter of fact I had a letter from her this morning. She still wants to come, so you'd better write to her yourself and offer her the accommodation.' He found the letter for which he was looking and passed it across the desk. 'Here's her address—I'll leave it to you to turn a blind eye to much of the letter's contents.'

He signed the letters she had already typed and passed those back to her.

'I see our advertisements for foreman, marine engineer and boy are in this morning's paper,' he said. 'I have to go into town later on. If by any chance anyone answers the ads. in person, you can interview them, can't you? And use your own discretion about taking them on. You'll be as good as I am—maybe better.'

She smiled. How could she ever have thought him difficult? 'I'll leave the particulars on your desk, anyway, if I do take anyone on.'

He gave her another curious look, and realizing all at once that she was in danger of giving herself away, she turned and went back to her own office. She really must watch herself. If he knew how she felt about him he would almost certainly be embarrassed and they would be quite unable to work together. He simply must not know.

She sat down at her desk and looked at the letter he had given her written by Celia. She saw the opening—*Darling Roger*—and could not help catching glimpses of the affectionate terms in which the letter was couched. She compressed her lips against the shafts of pain which went through her heart. What a complete idiot she was to have offered, for the second time, to give hospitality to Celia. She must have been out of her mind. But wasn't that thinking only of herself? If it would give him some pleasure to have Celia here—

Was he in love with her, Julia wondered, as she put a sheet of paper in her typewriter, or was she merely jumping to conclusions? Then she remembered the doodle and the photograph, and the answer was pretty conclusive. And why was he going to so much trouble regarding the house unless he had marriage in mind? He would tell her in his own time, she supposed. Celia had already seen over the house. If she were not reasonably sure that Roger loved Celia, Julia's thoughts went on, she might set about trying to attract him to herself. There were ways in which a woman could convey her feelings to a man and still keep her pride. But even as these thoughts came Julia rejected them. No matter what a woman did in her efforts to win a man there was still no guarantee that the man would fall in love with her. Love was something which could not be forced, and if a man loved a woman he usually found a way of letting her know it.

Julia tried to put an end to her thoughts about Roger. They were all too painful. Love brought happiness only when it was not demanding. She was not the first woman to love a man who did not love her. She would simply have to come to terms with it. If she could not without leaving, then she would have to leave and there was an end of it.

She typed a letter to Celia offering her accommodation in her houseboat for a holiday, being careful to exclude the dates on which her parents would be coming. When Roger came through to go out, she showed the letter to him.

He read it, then handed it back to her. ' This is most generous of you—but I must warn you, she's not likely to be very helpful domestically. You'll probably find yourself doing all the cooking and washing up and generally clearing up after her.'

'That—will be all right,' Julia answered, the fact that he knew Celia so well registering forcibly.

He went out saying he wouldn't be back until after lunch. He had been gone about half an hour when a young man knocked on the office door and said he had come in answer to the advertisement for a marine engineer.

'Sit down, won't you?' Julia invited, 'and I'll take your particulars. Mr Leighton is out at the moment, but—'

'I won't have to come again, will I? It's difficult to get time off except in my dinner hour.'

'No, I don't think you'll have to come back necessarily. We'll see. First, let me have your name, age and so on.'

His name was Tony Sheldrake, he had been out of his time for three years and had brought testimonials from three boatyards. They were good without being too glowing—which she would have been inclined to distrust, anyway. But then she noticed something else.

'These aren't very up-to-date, are they?' she asked. 'Where have you been working for the past twelve months? And where are you working now?'

'I've been at sea,' he said quickly. 'You know how it is. I wanted adventure and thought I'd sign up as a ship's engineer. But I didn't much care for it. I decided I'd rather have a shore job. The only thing is I threw my Board of Trade papers away. In any case, I'd have thought three references were enough.'

'Yes, I suppose they are.'

All three stated that they had found him 'honest and trustworthy' and testified to the work he had been doing on engines of all kinds.

'When would you be able to start?' she asked.

'Saturday, in time for change-over day, if you want me,' he answered promptly. 'I'm doing a one-off job at the moment. A big privately owned cruiser. The man wants it for Friday afternoon. That's why I can

110

only manage a dinner-hour for an interview.'

'I understand. Perhaps you'd like to see around the boatyard. I'll introduce you to our present foreman.'

She found Frank Willis and asked him privately to test the man's knowledge of marine engines as he showed him round. If he was satisfactory, she could see no good reason for keeping him hanging on for an answer on the off-chance of interviewing more applicants. Roger was anxious to get started on the job of expansion as soon as possible.

After about ten minutes had elapsed, Frank Willis came in search of her.

'He seems to know his stuff all right. In fact, if the guv'nor were to ask my advice I'd say he's more knowledgeable about marine engines than George. Still, you need a good man on maintenance, I suppose.'

'But you think he might be better working on the new auxiliaries?'

'Could be, but then George and I have worked together for a good long while and he's useful in other ways, too. Doesn't mind what he turns his hand to.'

Julia remembered something. 'Mr Leighton has said that he doesn't like breaking up a good team, but I'm glad to have your opinion anyway, Frank. I think we'll take him on.' She turned to move away, then halted. 'You—like him all right otherwise?'

Frank Willis hesitated. 'He seems pleasant enough. There's only one thing puzzles me.'

'And what's that?'

'This business of his being at sea for the past year. It seems odd to me, a man going from one kind of engineering to another like that. They're not the same.'

But Julia could see nothing amiss in that. 'Some people do have a period when they chop and change before settling down. I think he'll do.'

Before the week was out a yard foreman had also been engaged, interviewed by Roger himself. A small, round-faced, cheerful man in his fifties who loved boats and everything connected with them. Roger introduced him to Julia.

'This is Bob Winters, Julia. Until now he's been general foreman at Cootcraft which, as you know, is changing hands. So Mr Winters thought he'd make a change, too. Miss Barclay,' he went on, ' is my assistant. Anything you want to know, any queries of any kind can be referred to her just as well as to me.'

Julia silently blessed him. Her fears had been groundless. She was to remain as a sort of manager over all. And they certainly needed a yard foreman, especially on Saturdays, which could be chaotic. When David and Mr Hargreaves had been alive, one person could barely move from the office for the coming and going of holiday-makers. Saturday still remained the popular day for the start and finish of a holiday. Yachts and cruisers were brought in at ten o'clock and hired again by four at the latest. Between that time the boats had to be cleaned out from stem to stern, all the equipment checked, dirty linen replaced with fresh, the engines overhauled and filled up with fuel, the water tanks refilled, a fresh supply of liquid gas installed and the sailing tackle of the yachts and auxiliaries checked. All this while holiday-makers were coming and going, often getting in the way, those having reached the end of their holiday still not packed, the others anxious to get away before their boat was quite ready. Every available pair of regular hands with the addition of those of several cleaning women were needed on Saturdays.

Roger even consulted her before he finally engaged Bob Winters, and she herself interviewed a boy to take Andy's place for general duties.

' Right,' said Roger, an excited gleam in his eyes. ' Frank and his team can start right in on clearing out the shed the yachts have been housed in. There's enough material in stock for the conversion of the two half-deckers and to start the first hull of the new auxiliaries. Meanwhile, you and I have a date for lunch with the man who's going to draw our design.'

Suddenly life was good, life was exciting, Celia forgotten. Over lunch the special features of the new auxiliary yacht were discussed and rough sketches drawn until a final draft was decided upon.

'I'll post it on to you in a couple of days' time,' the designer promised.

Julia felt a deep sense of satisfaction, and her mind winged back to the past.

'David would have been pleased about this,' she said involuntarily.

'Who is David?' queried the designer.

'The son of the previous owner of Wingcraft. He and I often discussed a design like this. We put an idea to his father once, but he was reluctant to embark on something which might or might not pay off.'

'I should think this will pay off all right, once people know about it,' said the designer. 'But of course it takes time.'

Roger said nothing. There was a slight frown on his forehead and a thoughtful look on his face.

'Is anything wrong?' Julia asked him, imagining that he had thought of a snag with regard to the new design.

He shook his head, but said wearily: 'It's nothing that can be put right by drawing a design, at any rate.'

Julia wondered what he was driving at, and whether it had anything to do with Celia. She felt sure it had, and her day clouded over. It became more and more evident that he had something on his mind. When they had finished lunch he drove back to the boatyard in silence, and for the next few days Julia had very little conversation with him. She fought against hurt feelings. Her whole life, she supposed, would now revolve around him, but she must try not to feel hurt every time he was in a thoughtful mood and not imagine slights where none were intended.

Slowly, the summer advanced. Each Saturday morning saw the boatyard become more and more hectic as the number of craft being taken out increased. Soon there was not a craft which was not hired either for the week or fortnight, and Frank Willis and his team worked steadily on the conversion of the first of the half-deckers, then on building two others for day-hire, and finally making a start on the auxiliaries. Bob Winters was a splendid man to have about the place, pleasant, conscientious, tolerant with difficult holiday-makers and turning his hand to anything which required doing. The engineer, Tony Sheldrake, was not quite so satisfactory, to Julia's mind. He was slow, not a very good worker, and was often moody. If Bob Winters had a fault, he was too lenient. Within the first few weeks that the new engineer was with them several of the cruisers had engine trouble, a most unusual occurrence for Wing-craft. When she talked it over with Bob Winters, he told her not to worry.

'These things happen in the best of firms,' he said. 'You sometimes get a run of engine troubles. He seems all right, and he's had plenty of experience.'

And so Julia said no more at present, but she was determined to keep an eye on the man. It would be only too easy for the firm to lose its good reputation. Wingcraft did have clients who hired their boats year after year, but a ruined holiday could easily mean the loss of a customer in future and she felt responsible to Roger. She felt especially responsible with regard to this man as she had hired him.

Early in June, the fruit buds having formed in the apple orchards, Julia's parents came to stay in the house-boat for a week. Except for Saturday mornings, Roger insisted on her taking some time off to be with them, and one evening he took them all out to dinner himself, where there was dancing. Naturally, he and Julia danced together, and Julia stored up the memory of what it was like to be held in his arms. She sensed a restraint in the way he held her at first, then after a while he held her more closely and she gave herself up to the sheer pleasure of his nearness.

'You dance easily,' he said once during an encore. 'Have you done a lot?'

'We—ll, on and off, you know, One has spasms. David and I came here once or twice.'

'Oh, I see,' he said slowly.

She gave him a puzzled look. 'What do you see?'

'Nothing,' he said abruptly. 'Let's sit the rest of this dance out.'

He led her back to their table, and the next time they danced he held her so lightly and so far away it seemed he was almost afraid to touch her. She wondered why, and was reminded sharply of the existence of Celia.

A fortnight after her parents had gone back home, Celia was due for her stay in the houseboat. Since the night Max had left her in a huff, Julia had barely seen him, but she had wondered once or twice whether he had seen Celia and, if so, whether Roger was aware of it.

Oddly enough Max called at the houseboat one evening about three days before Celia's arrival. It was a pleasant evening, warm enough to take a canvas chair and sit beside the water. Max glanced around at the tubs and troughs of flowers Roger had had placed at intervals along the quaysides and either side of the office door.

'Hello—whose idea was this? Expecting Royalty?'

'It was Roger's idea—and I think it looks very nice. I wish I'd thought of it myself.'

He dropped on to the grass beside her chair. 'How are things? Sorry I haven't been round before. The old man's kept my nose to the grindstone. But then I don't suppose you've even missed me, have you?'

She smiled. 'I've wondered what's happened to you, yes, but of course I've been busy, too.'

'I'm sure you have. How's work on the new yachts going?'

115

'Making steady progress,' she told him briefly.

'And the new hands working all right?'

'Yes.'

He glanced up at her. 'I did hear that some of your cruisers had been having engine trouble.'

'How on earth did you come to hear of that?' she queried in surprise.

'Via my grapevine,' he answered.

She laughed briefly. 'It must be an extremely good one.'

'Actually, news does tend to travel rather fast on the Broads, but as a matter of fact I was out in one of our launches when I saw your man doing a spot of repair work.'

'How did you know he was our man?' she asked curiously.

'How did I— Well, I know your boats, don't I?'

'I suppose so.' She frowned. 'You know, I can't quite make that engineer out. He has good qualifications and all that, but we never used to have trouble with our engines.'

Max pursed his lips. 'Can happen,' he said laconically. 'Anyway, my sweet love, you've only had one season here, haven't you? I shouldn't be too hard on the poor man. Maintenance isn't a very enviable job. He'd probably be better on those new jobs you're building. Your other man used to be good on maintenance. Thought of swapping them over?'

Julia said she hadn't. 'It's up to Roger, anyway,' she added.

'Blast Roger,' said Max with sudden vehemence.

Julia glanced at him sharply. 'Max, don't start that again.' He didn't know she was in love with Roger, of course. All the same—

'Oh, I'm sorry,' Max said crossly. 'But it just seems all wrong somehow that—I mean, the place ought to be yours.'

'Well, it isn't, so there's no point in keeping going on about it. I'm perfectly happy as things are, anyway.'

' Are you? I have my doubts,' he insisted.

She sighed and to change the subject, she said: ' Has your grapevine told you that Celia—Miss Palmer is coming on a visit?' It was one way of finding out whether the two had had contact.

Max shook his head, but the fact that he showed no surprise gave her grounds for suspicion. He asked where Celia was staying and for how long.

' She's coming on Saturday, but I'm not sure for how long,' Julia told him. Then she asked directly: ' Have you seen her or heard from her since the time I saw you in Norwich?'

' Er—yes, I have as a matter of fact,' he said casually. ' She rang me up.'

' But why? Why should she ring you?'

' Why not?' countered Max.

' She's supposed to be engaged to Roger.'

' She's not engaged to him. At least, not at the moment. And even if she were—'

She's not engaged to him. If only it were completely true, Julia thought. But there was the indisputable evidence of the doodle, the photograph and numerous other things which told her that Roger was in love with Celia. Added to that, surely no woman would so blatantly pursue a man if she were not reasonably sure she was wanted. At any rate, no woman of Celia's class and undoubted attractiveness.

Roger came out of the house and started towards them, then halted and looked hard at Max before turning and going back again.

Julia half rose to her feet. ' I think he was looking for me. I'd better go and see what he wanted.'

' Don't be silly,' said Max. ' If he'd wanted you for anything he'd have come to you. Anyhow, you're off duty now, aren't you? Or don't you ever get any time off?'

' It isn't like that. I'm not paid by the hour,' she reminded him.

117

But the next moment she heard Roger's car start up and the roar of his engine as he drove off somewhere. She sank into her chair again rather uneasily. She felt sure he had wanted to speak to her but had changed his mind on seeing Max. Neither man liked the other and Julia could not really see that they had sufficient reason.

Celia was due to arrive in Norwich at twelve-thirty on the Saturday morning. Roger, naturally, went to meet her himself.

'I'll take her somewhere in town for lunch,' he told Julia, 'keep her out of your way for a little while. Then maybe you'd both have tea with me at the house. The worst will be over by four-thirty, I imagine,' he added, referring to the coming and going of the boat hirers.

She nodded. 'The boats will all be ready by then, anyhow, even if there are a few late arrivals, and Bob likes to stay around until they've all taken over.'

They stood in the doorway of the office for a few minutes and surveyed the busy scene. Bob Winters was guiding what must surely be the last of the large cruisers into a mooring space, the quayside was dotted with cars, holiday-makers—most of them wearing slacks and sweaters—going to and fro with their luggage, cleaning women with either buckets or clean linen, and, as it was a fine, sunny morning, some early arrivals sitting on the grass waiting to take over their boat without waste of a single minute.

'Nobody would think that they weren't supposed to take the boats over until four o'clock,' said Roger.

Julia smiled. 'It's astonishing how quickly they catch on. But it relieves the congestion if some of them do get away before four.'

Roger screwed up his face against the sun and watched Tony Sheldrake step ashore from a six-berth cruiser.

'The new men all working satisfactorily, would you say?' he asked.

Julia hesitated. She had never spoken to Roger about

the engineer, and during the last week or so there had been no troubles with the engines of the craft once the hirers had taken them out.

'Yes, I think we can safely say that,' she answered.

'Good.'

Another car drew up and a family of holiday-makers spilled out. Julia greeted them smilingly and went into the office to attend to them. She was very glad that Roger was taking Celia to lunch in the town. A sandwich lunch was all she would have time for herself, but she would have wanted to offer Celia something a little better than that, busy as she was. All the same, it was with a twinge of envy that she heard Roger drive off to Thorpe station. Lucky, lucky Celia!

It was four o'clock before Roger returned with their visitor, and she arrived looking radiant—like a woman in love, Julia thought with a pang.

'Did you have a good journey?' she asked Celia.

'Any journey would be good which brings me to Roger's side,' came the rather naïve reply.

Roger gave an amused—or was it an indulgent—smile. 'Have you nearly finished for the day, Julia?'

She nodded. 'There's only one more party to come, and Bob Winters will look after them.'

'Right, then we'll have tea. Mrs Harris has left it all prepared. I'll carry your bags round later, Celia.'

Julia asked to be excused while she tidied herself after her busy day, not only in the office but also lending a hand at the quaysides, handing out life-jackets, extra pillows, answering queries, and when everyone else was busy, helping to bring craft in to moor and giving them a push out. It was work she loved and she was in love with Roger, yet her heart was heavy. The wonderful sense of peace and happiness she had experienced when first she had acknowledged her love for Roger had been short-lived. Useless now to wish she had not invited Celia. In any case, she would merely have been putting off 'the evil day', she told herself. The day when Celia would be here permanently. Julia wondered again what they had quarrelled about. Was it because Roger had given up his secure job for his venture into the boat-hire business? It seemed very likely indeed. Roger was the sort of man who would do his best to make a woman happy, but she was certain he was too much of a man to allow a woman to dictate to him.

She washed her hands and face and changed her dress, then rather reluctantly went over to the house. The interior decorators—though having departed for the week-end—had finished their work on the lounge/dining room and had started on the bedrooms.

'It will be absolutely lovely when it's all finished, darling,' Celia was saying, as Julia entered. 'But what about the kitchen? *That* is simply frightful.'

Roger laughed. 'It's not too hot, I admit, but I thought we'd leave that until last. Mrs Harris is perfectly happy with it and anything too complicated might be too much for her. Later, of course—' He rose to his feet out of courtesy to Julia and offered her a chair.

'Shall I go and make the tea?' she asked, only too anxious to get away and wishing she had not come.

'Well, I don't really see—' Roger began, but Julia moved swiftly towards the door.

'I don't mind in the least,' she said. 'You stay and talk to Celia. I'll see to it.'

She glanced around the kitchen. It was not very modern or labour-saving, but it contained all the essentials. Somehow, Julia could not imagine Celia being very domesticated at all, but of course, one could never tell. For her own part, she would not care for a kitchen to look too computerized with a confusion of dials and switches. A decent cooker, a washer and spin dryer, good cupboards—

She pulled herself up sharply. She must stop dreaming, seeing herself even in the vaguest of terms as Roger's wife, mistress of his house.

The kettle was already full. Julia switched it on and

took the covers from the plates of food Mrs Harris had left prepared and carried them in. Roger and Celia had their heads together over something and did not even notice her entrance.

This, Julia told herself fiercely, was something she would just have to learn to live with. Or get away from. But she couldn't. Not now. She simply could not let Roger down with a busy holiday season before them.

She made the tea and took that in. Now Celia was telling Roger what kind of kitchen she would like.

'Of course I'm not very domesticated in a general sense, as you know, but I do like to cook now and then.'

Roger laughed. 'Does that mean your husband would only eat now and then? For my part, I find I have to eat every day, otherwise I grow kind of weak, if you know what I mean.'

This made even Julia smile, though she was not enjoying what she could only describe as Roger's 'love teasing'.

Celia laughed heartily, 'Oh, Roger, you are an idiot! You know perfectly well what I mean.'

Julia put her hand on the handle of the teapot to pour out, but suddenly Celia's hand shot out to stay her.

'I'll pour out, Julia, thank you.' Then she added sweetly: 'You've had such a busy day. You must be quite exhausted, and I do want to pull my weight.'

Julia let go the teapot and sat back, feeling put in her place very decidedly. Obviously Celia wanted her to know who was to be mistress of this house. As she poured the tea she became patronizing.

'Roger tells me what a treasure you are in the office and boatyard,' she said.

'I don't know about "treasure",' Julia answered. 'I just like the work, that's all.'

Celia smiled. 'Such an unusual job for a woman—messing about with boats and things.'

'I don't agree at all,' Julia came back. 'As long as

one likes the feminine things as well, I can see no reason why a woman can't enjoy those pleasures so often thought of as the masculine prerogative.'

'But, darling, I was talking about *work,* not pleasure. I'm hoping Roger will teach *me* to sail while I'm here. It's something I'm looking forward to enormously.''

Julia saw Roger's eyebrows raise slightly. 'Since when have you been interested in sailing, Celia?'

She gave him a provocative smile. 'Ever since you came to Norfolk, of course.'

Roger did not answer. He picked up a plate of sandwiches and offered it to Julia.

'Eat,' he said. 'You must be starving.'

Celia reverted to the topic of Julia and her efficiency. 'I'm so glad Roger *has* got someone like you to keep an eye on things. It means he'll be free to take me around—when we're not sailing, I mean. I suppose there are other things in Norfolk besides the rivers and Broads.'

'There are,' Roger told her. 'And it's a pity you didn't bring your own car. I'm afraid I shall be busy some of the time.'

'But of course you will, darling.'

As soon as she reasonably could Julia made her escape, pleading that she was tired. She did not even offer to do the washing up. She decided it would not hurt Celia to do that.

'Come just whenever it suits you to get settled in,' she told the other girl, giving her as warm a smile as she possibly could.

It was not going to be easy during Celia's stay, Julia knew that. Quite apart from the pain of seeing the man she loved with another woman, she sensed that Celia did not like her and resented her having daily contact with Roger. Perhaps, in the way women did know these things, Celia knew instinctively that Julia was in love with him.

About an hour later Roger brought Celia's luggage to

the houseboat. Julia viewed with dismay the two large suitcases. She had cleared the wardrobe of everything except her pony-skin coat, and had emptied two large drawers under one of the beds, but even so there would not be room for all the clothes Celia had evidently brought.

'Good gracious, I had no idea there would be such a shortage of hanging space,' Celia exclaimed. 'Perhaps if you could get rid of this coat—'

She took Julia's coat unceremoniously off its hook and thrust it at her.

Julia looked at the coat and frowned worriedly. 'I suppose I could hang it in the office for the time being.'

Celia shrugged and flung back the lid of one of her cases. 'My dear girl, I don't care what you do with it.'

Julia bit back a sharp retort. This woman was, after all, Roger's guest as well as hers.

'There are plenty of drawers,' she said, indicating the two spacious ones which were a standard fitment, forming the under part of each sleeping berth.

Celia glanced down at them—those under both berths. 'The four of them? They'll do, I suppose, though normally I don't like putting my clothes in drawers.'

Julia suppressed a sigh. 'The two under the right-hand berth are yours. My own clothes are in the other two.'

'Oh. Oh dear! This really is too bad. What a woman in love will suffer for the sake of her man! There's only one thing for it, I shall have to put some of my things in one of the rooms in the house.'

'Don't forget the workmen will be about the place come Monday,' Julia warned her. 'Surely, what there isn't room for in the wardrobe and drawers—and I think you'll find the drawers will hold more than you think —you can leave in one of your cases and the cases can be kept on the berth not in use.'

'Leave my clothes in a suitcase?' Celia echoed. 'I couldn't possibly do such a thing!'

Julia couldn't see why not and was beginning to wonder whether the other girl was being difficult deliberately.

'Well, I'm sorry, but I've offered you the best I can. I'll leave you to it,' she declared firmly.

Fortunately she had put her pony-skin coat in a polythene cover. There was nowhere in the saloon to hang it, so she took it across to the office and hung it there on its coat-hanger. She did not go straight back to the houseboat, she lingered on the quayside and gazed down river where at this time of the evening the water was still and the reflections barely distinguishable from the original. It was so beautiful here. She would never, normally, want to leave it. 'Home is where your heart is,' her father had quoted. Her heart was here with Roger, but if he belonged to someone else—

She was wondering whether to take one of the day launches out—there was no wind for sailing—when a car crunched on to the gravel and she turned to see Max. He waved and came towards her.

'Are you all through?' he asked.

She nodded. 'There's only one more, and Bob is seeing to that. All your people out?'

He grinned, '*I've* finished, anyway. I was wondering if you'd care to run into town and we could have a drink and supper somewhere.'

Julia agreed, glad of an opportunity to get away for a little while. When Ceila had finished unpacking she would undoubtedly pass the rest of the evening with Roger. She came to the door of the houseboat as Julia and Max were passing to the car. They greeted each other with a casual 'hello', and Julia could not help feeling that they knew each other far better than they wanted anyone to know.

'Finished your unpacking?' Julia asked her.

Celia shrugged. 'Well, I've found room in the cupboard that passes for a wardrobe for the essential things, but it's fearfully cramped. Are you going out?' Julia

124

said she was. 'Oh, well, don't wait up for me. Roger and I are going out presently and we shall probably be late.'

Julia would have liked to point out that as Celia would have to pass through her room to get to her own, there would be little use in going to bed, or at any rate trying to sleep. But what was the use? she thought. They had not made a very good start at all, and at this rate Celia's stay was going to be a very great trial indeed. She went into the houseboat to get a jacket which she had folded very carefully and placed uppermost in one of the drawers. Both bunks were scattered with Celia's clothes. She had brought enough luggage to last the whole summer. Surely for a holiday in the country a couple of drip-dry frocks, a cocktail dress and some slacks and sweaters would have been sufficient. There would have been plenty of room even for twice that amount, plus the usual warm coat, raincoat and spare shoes. But Celia appeared to have brought her entire wardrobe. Perhaps it had been a mistake to offer her accommodation. She would have been far better in a hotel.

When Julia went outside again, Celia and Max were talking together in low voices, and again came the feeling that there was something more between them than casual acquaintanceship.

During the course of the evening Max asked her how Tony Sheldrake, the maintenance engineer, was doing.

'Had any more troubles with the engines?' he queried.

Julia was glad to be able to answer that they hadn't.

'You haven't thought any more about swapping the two engineers over, then?' he pursued.

She hadn't thought another word about it. She certainly had not mentioned it to Roger, and she was beginning to wonder why Max should be so interested.

'Roger wanted our three old hands to work on the new craft,' she told him, and to her relief he changed the subject.

When they said goodnight he suggested that they should go for a sail the following day.

'How about it? But it will have to be one of yours. Father won't give houseroom to yachts.'

'Not even one for your own use?'

'Not even for my own use,' he affirmed with resigned bitterness.

There was an interval of silence—an embarrassed one for Julia. She could not understand this poor relationship Max evidently had with his father and she sometimes wished he were not quite so outspoken about it.

'Well, there's no problem,' she said after a moment or two. 'We can take out one of our half-deckers.'

'Good. And if it rains we can take a run out to Cambridge or somewhere.'

It did not rain, and Roger and Celia had the same idea—to go for a sail. As the boats were got ready, Julia could hear Celia talking incessantly, making a great show of wanting to know what everything was used for. Julia let go their moorings for them and watched them go with a pang, wishing it were she herself in the boat with Roger.

Max watched them go too, a smile of amusement on his face. 'And what time did Madam arrive back last night after her wild night out with dear Roger?' he asked.

Julia let the sneer go over her head. Of what use was it to keep getting angry whenever Max said something like that about Roger? He did not seem to know he was doing it.

'Oh, around eleven-thirty,' she answered, trying to sound casual, trying not to dwell on the dreamy look on Celia's face when she had come in.

'Do you want anything to eat or a drink?' Julia had asked her politely.

Celia had yawned extravagantly. 'Heavens, no! Roger and I had a lovely meal alone together. We decided not to go out after all. We thought we'd have

126

a nice cosy evening at home, just the two of us.'

Julia sighed impatiently and forced herself back to the present. The sail hoisted, Max let go the moorings and Julia swung the helm over and hauled in the sheet. But her heart was not in sailing this morning, and she very much doubted whether she would ever again find complete joy in the simple pleasure. The next few weeks, the rest of the season, indeed the whole of her life stretched out barren and useless without the love of Roger. She had loved David with a kind of brief, swift ecstasy, and a part of her had died too. But what she felt for Roger was like a burning, living flame which would remain within her for as long as she lived.

CHAPTER SEVEN

The half-decker was just turning into the main river when Max gave an exclamation.

'I've just remembered something. Do you mind if I slip back and use your phone? Don't bother to turn her round,' he added swiftly as she gave the helm a push, 'just pull into the bank and I'll walk along the edge and make my way by the back of the sheds.'

'All right.'

She brought the half-decker alongside the bank and let the sheet go free. Max jumped ashore and jabbed an anchor into the soft ground.

'The office will be locked,' she told him. 'But Bob Winters will give you the key.'

Bob was the only man on duty today. After working for some weeks with only short breaks, the boatbuilding team were taking an overdue Sunday off. The two half-deckers now had small cabins, the tops of which could be raised and lowered from amidships when required, and two entirely new ones built, tested and ready for hire. The building of the first of the new auxiliaries would begin in earnest tomorrow. There had been a little hold-up with the design of these. Frank Willis had found some fault in the first drafts and second drawings had been necessary.

Max was gone quite a long time. Julia began to feel restless and wondered what on earth was keeping him. At last he appeared, smiling and apologetic.

'Sorry and all that, Julia. First I couldn't find Bob—he'd found a quiet spot to fish, then when I took the key back we got talking. Once Bob starts he doesn't know when to stop. I couldn't get away.'

Julia made no answer. It was true that Bob liked to talk, but she felt it hardly fair of Max to speak that way of him. It was not worth pursuing, however, and as

128

soon as Max had let go the moorings and jumped aboard she set the nose of the yacht to the open river which led to Barton Broad. She fully expected that Celia and Roger would have sailed in the same direction. The Broad was a very beautiful one and the way to it extremely pleasant and picturesque. Max and herself might or might not catch them up. It would depend, Julia thought, on how much sailing tuition Roger was giving Celia. Lucky Celia!

'Hey, you're daydreaming, aren't you?' Max said suddenly as she allowed the craft to sail too closely to some broken piling. 'Let me take over.'

She relinquished both helm and sheet without a word and sat down to one side, resting her arms on the cabin top, barely noticing the pale blue sky and the drift of milky cloud, the swaying reeds and the wild life. All she could see was Roger's face, and all she could feel was a great ache in her heart.

Max and herself did not catch up with Celia and Roger at all, and there was no sign of them on the Broad.

'Maybe they've gone up to Neatished or Sutton,' said Max.

But when they returned to the boatyard themselves, the other boat was already tied up at its moorings and Roger was in the act of stepping aboard the high-powered launch they kept for emergencies like towing craft home or getting them out of difficulties. He looked extremely worried.

'What's happened?' Julia asked swiftly.

'One of our six-berth cruisers is stuck on Breydon Water,' he answered. 'It's already got a list and the tide is running out fast. I thought Bob had better stay here until you came back.'

'Shall I come with you? That is, if Bob will stay here for a little while longer.'

Whether Roger heard or not, he pulled the self-starter without answering.

'I should go, Miss Barclay, if I were you,' Bob

Winters murmured in her ear. 'If the tide is running out—and it is, by the look of things—he may find it more difficult than he realizes. You're more used to handling these boats and one of you might be needed to get more help. Meanwhile I'll get in touch with the Yarmouth Harbour Master and ask him to keep a look out.'

Roger looked up. 'Will someone let go the moorings for me?'

'Jump in, miss, I'll do it,' said Bob.

Julia stepped lightly into the launch and took the front passenger seat.

Roger glanced at her swiftly. 'You don't have to come—unless you really want to.'

'I want to,' she answered.

As soon at the launch was free of its moorings Roger opened the throttle, and once clear of the dock he sent the launch as fast as regulations allowed in the direction of Breydon Water—that expanse of water, once an estuary of the North Sea.

'What happened to the cruiser to make her drift on to the mud?' asked Julia.

'Engine trouble, I gather. Then they just drifted, I suppose.'

'Engine trouble? But that's terrible. Think of the damage to our reputation!'

'I *am* thinking of it. And I don't like it,' Roger answered shortly.

Julia frowned. 'I simply don't understand it. This is something that's never happened before to one of Wingcraft's boats, I'm sure of it.'

Roger took a deep breath. 'There's a first time for everything, I suppose.'

'But this is serious. It should *never* happen. Our engines are checked each time they're taken out. We've had too many instances of engine trouble this year for them to be put down to " accidents ".'

Roger gave her a swift glance. 'What are you driving at exactly?'

Julia hesitated, but she simply had to say what was in her mind, and she felt sure the same thing would be in Roger's thoughts.

'I think I made a mistake in hiring Tony Sheldrake. He has not turned out to be such a good engineer, after all.'

'You think you should give him notice?'

'It seems the only thing to do. I was with the firm all last summer and we never had one engine fault. It's something David and his father prided themselves on.' Then she remembered what Max had said. 'Of course, it could be that he's better at general fitting than maintenance. You—wouldn't consider swapping him and George around—putting George back on maintenance and letting Sheldrake work on the new yachts with Frank?'

Roger thought for a moment, then said quietly but decidedly: 'No.'

Julia took a sidelong glance at his face and was surprised at the toughness she saw there.

'I'm—sorry,' she jerked out. 'It was only a tentative suggestion. I don't want to be harsh or unjust towards the man, and it's never very pleasant giving a man the sack.'

'You could give him another chance.'

But Julia shook her head. 'He's had plenty of chances already. We simply can't risk another Breydon Water incident. If we don't get them off in time they could be stuck there until the next tide, and that can be a very nasty experience for anyone on holiday. It would be enough to put them off a Broads holiday for life. Or if not for life, they would never hire one of our craft again—neither would a great many more people. News like this travels fast along the rivers and Broads.'

'Very well. Perhaps you'd like me to take the unpleasant task off your hands.'

But she couldn't let him do that. 'That's very good of you, but I think I'd prefer to do it myself,' she answered.

By keeping up a good speed and cutting off corners they reached Breydon Water in just over half an hour. A brisk wind was blowing from the seaward side, making the water choppy, and as Roger put the engine to full speed small waves broke over the bows and slapped on the foredeck. Julia picked up the binoculars and swept the wide area. A few cruisers having left it almost too late to deal with the mill-race current which would surge through Yarmouth harbour were headed in that direction. The rapidly falling tide was showing wide expanses of mud outside the marked channel and in a number of places the blackened and ugly teeth of the old wooden revetment broke through the brown water.

'Can you spot her yet?' Roger asked, a note of anxiety in his voice.

'I think—yes. There she is, near marker twenty-four, about half a mile away.'

Roger kept the launch to the centre of the channel. In a few minutes they were almost up with the grounded cruiser and Julia could make out the shallow-draught inshore rescue bobbing about close to the cruiser. Roger took the launch as close in as he dared. Julia saw the anxious faces of the holiday crew as she was picking up a ready coiled throwing line. She threw it expertly so that it fell right across the rescue launch.

'Good,' Roger called to her. 'Take over the wheel while I pass the towing warp. It's too heavy for you to handle.'

Julia took his place and held the engine at slow ahead so that the pull of the falling tide held the launch about stationary. She watched the distance between herself and the listing cruiser anxiously as Roger bent the warp on to the throwing line, then passed it yard by yard to the crew of the rescue launch, one of whom made it fast on to the stern of the cruiser. Then Julia

132

went astern slowly, turning by degrees until the towing
rope was over their stern and tight enough not to foul
their propellor. She faced about with her hand still on
the wheel. Roger signalled to her to increase speed.
The warp vibrated under the strain, throwing off drops of
water like a dog shaking itself. The rescue launch also
added its power and the threshing screws of both churned
up a brown muddy foam. For some minutes the cruiser
would not move from the black, clinging ooze, then Julia
gave a cry of relief.

'I think she's moving, Roger.'

'It's doubtful. We need just a little more power.'
He cupped his hands and called to a youngish man on the
cruiser, 'Could you jump into your dinghy and come
alongside our bows?'

The man waved in reply and a few strokes on his oars
and the outward run of the tide brought him alongside
the cruiser's bows. Julia watched, puzzled for a moment
by the manoeuvre. Then she saw Roger lower the
launch's kedge anchor into the stern of the dinghy and
begin paying out the chain.

'I apologize for making you work,' he said to the
man, 'but if you row out as far as you can, then throw
the anchor overboard it might just do the trick.'

'That's all right. I'm finding it quite exciting.'

Julia managed a smile although she was feeling a little
strained. She ought to have thought of this trick too,
ferrying the anchor out and using the launch's winch
to get further hauling power.

The anchor splashed to the bottom. Roger began
working the winch. The stern of the cruiser swung a
little, then with a great sucking sound she slid into clear
water. Julia immediately lowered her engine speed.
Roger ran aft and hauled the warp in to make a short
tow rope.

'Which way were you going?' he said to the man
in the dinghy.

'We had planned to spend the night in Yarmouth.

That's where we were going when the engine cut out.'

'Right. We'll tow you there and send a man along first thing in the morning to look at it.'

Others aboard the cruiser were a middle-aged couple and a younger woman along with two children, a girl and a boy, obviously all of the same family.

'I do apologize for any inconvenience caused,' Roger said before they left the holiday-makers. 'And I hope you were not too alarmed by what happened.'

Julia noticed that the elder of the two men said nothing. He could be a difficult customer to placate. But his wife smiled and so did the younger woman, though the older one admitted the experience had been a little frightening.

Roger and Julia set off back to the boatyard, Roger navigating as before. Julia stole a glance at him.

'I think I ought to congratulate you on the way you handled things there.'

'Oh?' he answered. 'Did you think I wouldn't be able to?'

'No-o, but you can't have had a lot of experience of that sort of thing.'

'I'm used to facing difficult engineering problems, so there was nothing to it really.'

But Julia considered he was being modest, and the way he had handled the situation added to her admiration of him.

The following morning Julia called Tony Sheldrake into her office.

'I expect that by now you have heard what happened yesterday,' she began.

He shrugged. 'I hope you're not blaming me. The engine was perfectly all right when I sent her out on Saturday.'

Julia picked up her paper knife. 'I'm sorry to have to say this, but this sort of thing has never happened before with Wingcraft.'

'Then you've just been lucky, haven't you?' he threw

134

out insolently.

She eyed him calmly. 'No, Mr Sheldrake, I don't think it was a matter of luck at all. We simply had a good maintenance engineer.'

'And I'm not?'

It was Julia's turn to shrug. 'Perhaps you don't really like maintenance work. But whether you do or not, if you have no explanation to offer about the failure of the cruiser's engine, I think it would be best if you found employment elsewhere. I don't think you'll have any difficulty.'

'You're darned right I won't,' he said unpleasantly. 'I was a fool to take this job, anyway, but I was only marking time. Do you want me to go now—today? In which case—'

Julia shook her head. 'No, you can find out what's wrong with the engine of the cruiser and put that right, if you will, then leave on Friday. We will, of course, pay you the full week's wages. If you left today, you would naturally forfeit a week's wages.'

She felt she had to be firm with the man. It had been a mistake to take him on, she realized that now. Quite apart from his offensiveness, there was something about his whole manner which she could not quite lay her finger on. She certainly did not feel she could ever trust him again.

He gave another shrug and strolled to the door. 'All right, Friday it is, then. It suits me.'

She made a mental note to tell Bob Winters to supervise the man very closely and certainly to check over the cruiser's engine before it went on its way. She went through to the inner office to tell Roger what she had done. He nodded his approval.

'I've been having a talk with George,' he said. 'And he's willing to take care of maintenance as well as fit out the new craft. Strictly speaking there's not a lot for him to do on the new auxiliaries at this stage, and if he's willing to go from one job to the other, we shan't

135

need another engineer. Maybe what we need most is a general yard man—a good all-rounder, one who can turn his hand to anything, what used to be called a " Jack of all trades and master of none ", though you don't hear the expression much nowadays.'

Julia agreed that such a man might be more useful than a qualified engineer. ' But I'd rather you did any future hiring,' she told him.

He gave her one of his penetrating looks. ' I will if you like—but don't be afraid of making a mistake. The man who never made a mistake never made anything. I'm sure you've heard that saying, and it's true.'

She smiled, loving him with all her heart. ' You're very—kind and understanding.'

But at this he frowned. ' Kind and understanding? Nonsense. It's common sense. But we won't advertise for a man, I'll have a word with Frank Willis. He may know of someone.'

He lowered his eyes to some papers on his desk and she felt herself dismissed. There was a great knot of pain in her heart, and she knew she was never going to be able to feel normal in his presence ever again. She would always know either joy or pain.

He looked up again suddenly. ' Was there something else?'

She tried to take herself in hand. ' There—was one other thing. Do you think it would be a good idea to offer the hirers of the cruiser a rebate for inconvenience caused? It might make all the difference to their attitude, and consequently our reputation.'

' Thank you. It's nice of you to be so concerned about " our reputation ". And I do think it's a good idea. I had the same thing in mind.'

' Oh. Oh, I see. Perhaps you'll let me know the amount before the week-end, then I can give it to them when they hand the cruiser in.'

' I will.' Again, there was that tone of dismissal.

She went back to her own office worried and unhappy.

What was wrong with him this morning? Even allowing for her heightened sensitivity where he was concerned, there was something. When he had repeated the words ' our reputation ' he had almost been sarcastic. Was it that he still did not trust her, at heart, to be wholehearted about the interests of his boatyard, that he still thought she was hankering after ownership for herself The thought hurt her beyond belief.

The sound of a motor engine starting up brought her out of her thoughts and she went outside to see Tony Sheldrake in the driving seat of the van, obviously going to where they had left the cruiser moored last night.

' Just a moment, Mr Sheldrake! ' she called out. ' I think Bob should go with you. You can better show him where the fault is. We don't want a second breakdown.'

' Suit yourself,' was the man's answer.

Bob Winters did not altogether like the idea of going with the engineer, but Julia made him see that it was both best and wisest.

' And I don't think you could hurt that man's feelings —or pride. I don't think he cares two hoots about anything,' she added.

As the two men drove away Celia emerged from the houseboat looking fresh and attractive in a sleeveless shift dress, making Julia feel very workaday in her jeans and shirt blouse. Nevertheless, she forced a smile.

' Morning, Celia. Have you had breakfast?'

' If you call a cup of tea breakfast, yes. Where's Roger?'

' In his office. Would you like me to come and cook something for you?'

' No, thanks. I'll go across to the house and make coffee for Roger and myself.'

Julia crossed to the houseboat knowing she would have to straighten things up. Celia was not a very tidy person and Julia tried not to be too critical of her, but it wasn't easy, especially when she was pointedly excluded as she had been just now. As she made Celia's bed and cleared the table Julia had to fight down resentment very hard indeed.

She heard the telephone ringing loudly from the outside extension bell. After a few minutes it stopped, so she concluded that Roger was answering it. She glanced through the window of the houseboat and saw him come to the door. He called out and beckoned to her.

'It's for you,' he said as she hurried across to the office.

Celia appeared at his side, and together they walked across to the house. Julia was not sure how much longer she could stand this. She picked up the receiver from her desk to find it was Max at the other end of the line.

'How'd you get on last night?' he enquired. 'Sorry I couldn't wait until you got back, but I didn't know how long you were going to be.'

She told him briefly how Roger and she had managed to ease the cruiser off the mud of Breydon Water and into the channel and how good Roger had been.

'And I suppose the blame for the engine failure rests squarely on the shoulders of Tony Sheldrake?'

'Well, the engines *are* his responsibility,' she pointed out. Then she added: 'Or *were*.'

'You don't mean you've given the poor so-and-so the sack?'

'He leaves on Friday.'

'Good lord, that's a bit much, isn't it? You certainly don't believe in giving second chances, do you?'

Julia coloured, but she stuck her ground. 'That's not true. And Tony Sheldrake has had plenty of second chances. We have our reputation to consider.'

'We? You talk as though you're in partnership or something with Leighton.'

He said it as if the possibility was too remote to take seriously.

'One doesn't have to be in partnership to feel responsible,' Julia told him. 'And I must ring off now, Max.

138

I have things to do.'

'Okay. Well I'll drop round and see you this evening,' he said lightly, and without waiting to hear whether she agreed or not, he said goodbye and rang off.

She sat down at her desk and tried to deal with the correspondence. She thought and half hoped that Roger would come and ask her to have coffee with him and Celia, but he didn't. He waited until Bob Winters and Tony Sheldrake returned, heard their report on the engine trouble, then sought her out and told her he was taking Celia out to lunch.

With a heavy sigh Julia went to have a few words with Bob Winters herself.

'What was the trouble, Bob?' she asked him.

'Dirt in the injector,' he told her. 'For some reason or other the filter wasn't in. Tony swears he didn't leave it out—and it's not the sort of thing an engineer would *forget* to put in, still less *take* out. You see,' he enlarged, 'once the filter is in place, it's rarely necessary to look at the thing again—or maybe once during the season to clean it out.'

Julia gave a puzzled frown. 'I don't quite understand. Surely it's a part of the engine and the question of taking out or putting in—except to clean it—shouldn't arise. And if what you say is correct—and I'm sure it is—either somebody took it out to clean and *did* forget to put it back, or else took it out deliberately.'

'Somebody who knows nothing about engines could have been—messing about and thought it wasn't important,' Bob suggested tentatively.

'Who? The hirers?' She shook her head. 'Mr Leighton asked them last night if they'd done anything to the engine, and they said they hadn't, beyond taking a general look—and seeing nothing obviously wrong. In any case, they're not given any tools, so they couldn't.'

'I know.'

'Then who—'

139

Bob Winters turned away. 'I'd rather not say any more, Miss Barclay. Sheldrake tells me he's leaving on Friday, anyway, so we might just as well forget the whole business.'

'Not entirely, Bob,' she said quietly. 'From now until Friday I'd like you to supervise him closely.'

He nodded. 'That's what I'm here for anyway.'

Julia puzzled all day, on and off, about what Bob had told her. He had been reluctant to let her believe that Tony Sheldrake would leave out or take out the filter deliberately. Yet he had said himself that it was not the sort of thing an engineer would forget. But why should Sheldrake do such a thing? In the end, rather than think the worst of him, she forced herself to the conclusion that he had taken it out to clear it and only *thought* he had put it back again. The man did not appear to be unduly upset about leaving, she told herself, and she would be glad to see him go.

She did not see very much of Roger for the rest of the day, although that wasn't really surprising. By common consent Monday was regarded as his day off, and Wednesday hers, neither being very busy days. But so often he did not take it, and nor did she in the sense that they went out a great deal. But today he rang after lunch to say that he and Celia would not be back until late evening.

'We've decided to make a day of it,' he said. 'There's so much more of Norfolk Celia hasn't seen—and it's such a lovely day.'

It *was* a lovely day. It was warm, there was barely a cloud in the sky, thrushes were feeding their young, butterflies flitted to and fro among the tall grass in the meadow, and the air was filled with the sound of bird song and the perfume of roses from nearby gardens. A lovely, lovely day, except that for Julia there was no music in her heart, only desolation, and in her sky, dark clouds. She tried to thrust thoughts of Roger and Celia out of her mind, but the day dragged as she answered the telephone, dealt with enquiries, let out day boats for hire, and did general odd jobs around the boatyard. Though she had not really been looking forward to Max coming, she found she was almost glad to see him when he arrived about seven.

'Have you eaten?' she asked him.

'Well, I had tea about a couple of hours ago. I'll peck a little more, if you're inviting me. Or could we go out somewhere?'

'No, I'd rather not leave the place, in case something happens. I haven't eaten much myself since lunch, so if fruit juice and a ham salad will suit, then cheese and biscuits—'

'Sounds great. Lead me to it!'

The meal did not take long to serve. Not wanting to eat alone again, Julia had hoped Max would join her, and had the salad all prepared in the little refrigerator of the houseboat, the fruit juice ready chilled. Max kept up a chatter of generalities for which she was grateful, even though she only half heard some of it. But when he said suddenly, 'The two lovebirds out for the evening?' her heart twisted painfully.

'If you're referring to Roger and Celia, I'd hardly call them that,' she answered after a pause.

He eyed her shrewdly. 'My dear girl, why don't you face it? She's twisting him around her little finger. You don't suppose she's here just for the good of her health, do you? And if he wasn't encouraging her, she wouldn't still be here. Now would she, I ask you?'

Julia held her breath, then let it out swiftly. 'You're only guessing, Max, aren't you? In any case it's none of our business.'

'No? It could be. And I'm not guessing entirely. I was talking to Celia for about a couple of hours last night while you and dear Roger were rescuing the cruiser, and she told me quite a lot—in a roundabout way. They had an unholy row back in London, but they're rapidly becoming reconciled. He wants her to come and live here, of course, that's why he's having the house done up. But she prefers London and she's hoping to lure him back there.'

Julia made no answer. What was there she could say? Max was only confirming what she already felt certain of in her own mind, at least with regard to the way Roger felt about Celia. But Max went on talking.

' Of course, if she succeeds—and I'm sure she will because a woman usually gets her own way in the end if a man loves her—then that's where you'll come in.'

' I?' she asked sharply.

She put two plates of ham and salad on the table, then sat down and pushed the plate of brown bread and butter towards him.

Max looked at her for a few minutes, then said emphatically: ' Yes, you. Or have you changed your mind completely about wanting this place?'

Julia did not answer immediately. Was it possible that ownership of the boatyard had once meant so much to her? She had been so sure that Roger had settled down here, that Celia would join him here when they were married. She had not thought of the possibility of Celia persuading him back to London. It it did happen, would she want to make him an offer to stay on, after all? She shook her head vigorously, feeling dangerously near to tears.

' No. No, I wouldn't want to stay on now, whether Celia persuaded him or not.'

' You've quite made up your mind, then?' asked Max eyeing her keenly.

' Max, I've told you—' she burst out raggedly. ' Just as soon as I reasonably can, I'm going back home. And now, if you don't mind, I'd rather not talk about it any more.'

Max shrugged and began to eat. ' You do get yourself het up about things, don't you? Maybe you would be happier " down on the farm " at that.'

Again Julia made no reply. Max had no idea how she

felt about Roger. He had made tentative guesses, but how could she explain to anyone, even if she wanted to, the depth of her feelings? If he had even the smallest conception he would not speak that way—as if she were 'het up' about nothing. Was it nothing to be in love with a man and watch him with another woman? It was going to be difficult enough to forget him with a hundred miles or so between them, but here, at the boatyard, she would be for ever reminded. It was odd that she had not *wanted* to forget David, but though she loved Roger far more deeply she felt the memory of him would always be more of a pain than a joy.

Max asked her how the building of the first of the new auxiliaries was getting on, and she told him that a good start had been made.

'Everything going according to plan—or in this case design?'

'Yes, of course. Why shouldn't it?' she asked sharply.

'I'm only asking out of interest,' he protested at her tone. 'I don't know what's come over you these days, Julia.'

She felt ashamed. There really was no reason why she should let her unhappiness spill over on to Max.

'I'm sorry. I'm afraid things are getting me down a little. Let's have some music, shall we?'

She put on a record and tried to ease the weight of depression, but long after she wished Max would go, he stayed on. She was so physically tired, she was almost dropping to sleep when the sound of a car was heard outside.

Max grinned. 'Your lodger, I expect. I think I'd better go now. It's late.'

He stood up and so did Julia to see him off. Then to her surprise he suddenly pulled her towards him and before she could stop him he took her in his arms and kissed her firmly on the lips. For a moment she couldn't move, he was holding her so tightly and so close to him.

143

Then the door opened and Celia stood there. Max laughed and let Julia go abruptly, and through the window she saw Roger turn away. He got into his car again and drove it towards his garage.

Celia gave an amused smile. 'Well, well. Sorry I butted in. I didn't realize—'

'It's all right. I was just going,' Max said casually. ''Night, Julia darling. Be seeing you. 'Night, Celia.'

He was gone before Julia could say a word. The whole thing had happened so swiftly. She drew an angry breath.

'Really, Max makes me so angry!' she exploded

Celia laughed. 'I don't see anything to be angry about. Max is a very attractive man. Why don't you marry him? I feel sure he's asked you.'

'I don't happen to be in love with him,' Julia answered.

Celia continued to smile. 'Pity. Still, you could do worse. I don't know that it's so necessary to be in love with the man you marry.'

Julia stared at her. 'How can you say such a thing? Aren't you in love with—' She stopped short, suddenly realizing that she had very little to go on and that she was probably jumping to a great many conclusions about Roger and Celia.

But Celia took her up. 'With Roger, you were going to say? Of course. But more important still is that *he* is crazy about *me*.'

Julia felt she would suffocate. She filled the kettle and set it on the cooker to boil.

'Why—is that more important?' she asked jerkily. 'I would have thought your own feelings were the more important to *you*.'

Celia shook her head. 'No, no. To be very much in love with a man makes a woman too vulnerable. The thing is to have a man who really is gone on you.'

Julia was staggered. 'You just *have* to be joking, Celia.'

But Celia merely laughed. 'I *want* Roger, make no mistake about that. And I mean to have him. As a matter of fact, he's asked me to marry him, but I haven't given him my answer yet.'

'Why not?' Julia forced herself to ask.

'To keep him guessing, of course. It's good for a man.'

Julia felt she could bear this kind of talk no longer. 'Do you want a drink, Celia, or anything to eat?'

Celia yawned. 'No, thanks. I've had plenty to eat and drink all evening. I'm ready to go to bed now.'

Julia was thankful at last to see the dividing door between Celia and herself, but tired as she was, she felt she would not be able to settle down to sleep without a little air. She slipped a jacket over her shoulders and went outside. The air was sweet and fresh. She stood for a moment to adjust her eyes to the darkness and took a few long breaths, expelling deeply as if the act would clear her heart and mind of the pain and agony of loving a man who was in love with someone else.

She walked towards the water, now black as the sky above. What was she going to do? To get right away from the scene was the obvious answer. But wouldn't that be rather selfish? Roger had no idea how she felt and she could not possibly tell him. What earthly reason could she give him for leaving in the middle of the season? She couldn't let him down just to spare her own feelings.

Suddenly she halted as she saw a shadow by the boathouse which was being used for the work on the new craft. Who could it possibly be at this hour? Frank and his team were not working all night and no one was allowed in there except the workmen and Roger and herself. She called out and her heart contracted violently as Roger himself answered.

'Julia?' he counter-questioned sharply. 'What on earth are you doing out here?' As he spoke he walked towards her and when he reached her side it was apparent, even in the dim light from the stars and the houseboat some yards away, that he was displeased about something. Unhappy because Celia was making him wait for his answer? But at the moment he was waiting for her own.

'I'm—just getting a breath of fresh air,' she told him.

He turned and looked towards the black velvet of the river. 'Been cooped up all evening, have you?' he asked in a strange voice.

'Well, yes. Max came, and I hadn't eaten, so we had a meal together.'

'Very cosy, I must say.'

His tone sent a swift stab of pain through her heart. 'You disapprove?'

Through the window he had seen Max kissing her, of course, and doubtless thought they had spent the whole evening lovemaking.

'It's none of my business what you do when you're not working for me,' he answered brusquely.

This was even worse. She almost burst into tears. She *wanted* what she did to be his business.

'All the same,' he continued, 'I think it would be better if you could find somewhere else to live other than the boatyard. Couldn't you find a flat?'

He couldn't have hurt her more if he had dealt her a physical blow. But now she was beyond tears. She rounded on him.

'So you want to get rid of me, do you? Well, don't worry, Mr Leighton, you'll soon be rid of me altogether. I was going to leave at the end of the season in any case, but in view of what happened tonight—'

He grasped her by the shoulders. 'I want to get rid of you? Don't talk such nonsense. And why were you going to leave at the end of the season? Not because you're going to marry that no-good Max Windham. That I would not believe.'

'And why not?' she flashed back, hardly aware of what she was saying, aware only of his hands bruising her shoulders.

'Because you're not in love with him, that's why. You're in love with a ghost, aren't you? A ghost called David who—'

She cried out and covered her face with her hands, unable to take any more from him and feeling as though her heart would break.

There was an exclamation from Roger. Unexpectedly, his arms came about her and he held her close to him, resting her head on his shoulder.

'Julia, I'm sorry. I shouldn't have said that. It—it just makes me mad to see that fellow around the place. I can't stand him somehow, and—I've had one hell of a day, one way and another. Forgive me—please.'

For a second or two nothing mattered except that— magically—she was in his arms, but the mention of his difficult day coupled with what Celia had told her brought her to a true realization of things. Her heart torn with pity for him and pain for herself, she pushed against him and freed herself.

'It's—all right, I understand. There are times when I—don't much like Max myself. At others, he's bearable.' Pride prevented her from saying that almost any company is better than none when you're lonely. 'I can tell him not to come again, if you like,' she offered.

'No, no.' He put his hand under her arm and led her towards the bank of the river. 'You came out for some air and I picked a quarrel with you. I'm sorry. And please forget what I said about the houseboat. I should have learned by now to keep a better control over both my tongue and temper. Instead of saying things to you like I did I should have been thanking you for having Celia. It can't have been easy for you.'

Julia tried to reassure him without actually lying. 'I haven't minded in the least,' she said. 'I only hope she's been comfortable and has enjoyed her stay.'

'I think she has, but she's not a great lover of the country. She's happier in the city where there are lots

147

of shops and theatres, and plenty going on of the kind of thing she likes.'

'Will you—ever go back to London, do you think?' she ventured to ask, and held her breath for his reply.

He leaned against a willow and gazed out on to the water. 'I don't know. As of this moment, I don't want to. It depends on—so many things—or maybe only one.'

There was a moment of silence. Julia was treasuring every moment of this time alone with him, this precious, quiet conversation, even though his mind *was* occupied with thoughts of Celia.

'Some—decisions are hard to make,' she said. Then she added, wanting only his happiness and remembering Celia's extraordinary ideas about love: 'I should think that if you find yourself torn two ways about a course of action, it's best to wait until you're absolutely *certain* you're doing the right thing. It's so easy to make the wrong decision by trying to make up your mind too quickly. It's unsettling, I know, but—'

He turned and smiled at her and her heart gave a small leap of pleasure.

'I think that's very sound advice. I'll take it.' He put a hand on her shoulder for good measure. 'Maybe it's the sort of advice you should follow for yourself too. And now I think you'd better go and get your beauty sleep. It's getting chilly out here.'

Her treasured moments were over. He walked with her to the houseboat and they said goodnight. Celia's light was out. Julia let herself in quietly and locked the door, feeling a little more at peace with herself. At least she had probably influenced him into not giving way to Celia about going back to London. Celia did not love him, Julia felt sure. At least, not the way he deserved to be loved. She shut her ears to the voice which told her that if Roger took a chance and put off making his decision about going back to London, this might result in Celia deciding to stay here with him and marrying him. She went to sleep with the feel of his arms about her, her head resting on his shoulder.

She woke up the following morning feeling happy too, until she heard Celia call out from the other room: 'Julia, have you made any tea yet?'

'Won't be a minute,' Julia answered, putting her feet to the floor with the realization that nothing was changed. Roger was still in love with Celia. His conversation last night had shown that.

She set the kettle on to boil and made morning tea, then took it in to Celia. The weather had changed during the night, and rain was now slanting down sharply, drumming monotonously on the roof of the houseboat.

'You're awake early this morning,' she told Celia. 'It's only half past seven.'

Celia glanced at her bedside clock. 'It isn't, you know. It's half past *eight*. You're late.'

Julia put her wrist watch to her ear. 'Good heavens, so I am! I must have forgotten to wind my watch last night.'

She handed Celia her tea and received a cool, speculative glance.

'By the way, did you go out last night after I'd gone to bed?'

'Only for a breath of air.'

'I could have sworn I heard a man's voice.'

Julia temporized. It might be wisest not to mention her late-night *tête-à-tête* with Roger, if it could be avoided.

'Really?' she answered. 'But I'll have to fly. I'd just hate it if Roger were in the office before me.'

Later on in the morning, it occurred to her that perhaps Roger objected to Max coming to the boatyard because of Celia. He might not be as ignorant of their meetings as was supposed. The thought gave her little comfort.

The rain continued, on and off, for the rest of the week.

Celia became more and more bored, and more and more irritable.

'Imagine spending the rest of your life in a dump like this!' she deplored one afternoon during a particularly heavy shower.

'You call green fields, an open sky and a clear flowing river a dump? Then what would you call the slums of London?' Julia asked her quietly.

'I don't happen to live in a slum,' Celia retorted. 'I don't know how you can stand it. I'd be bored to tears.'

'It's having nothing to do which makes you bored,' Julia told her.

'Well, I'm on holiday, aren't I? Roger won't leave his work to take me out—and heaven knows he has enough people working *for* him. Why he has to do *any*, I can't imagine. If he wants to hang on to the place as an additional interest, I can't see why he doesn't hire a manager. After all, it's only a couple of hours from London on the train, and not much more by road in a decent car. I shall have a word with him about it.'

But towards the end of the week something happened which gave Roger plenty to worry about besides Celia.

Frank Willis came into the outer office looking extremely worried.

'What's the matter, Frank?' asked Julia.

'It's the new auxiliary, Miss Barclay. It's not really turning out as it should. Either there's something wrong with that design or my name's not what it is.'

'But—but that's impossible. I mean—'

'That's what I thought, but we're following it in every detail and—' He broke off. 'Is Mr Leighton in his office? If so, I'd better have a word with him, too.'

Roger was in. Julia tapped on his door and went in, followed by Frank. Roger looked up from his desk in surprise.

'What's this—a deputation?'

Julia came straight to the point. 'It's the new auxiliary,' she told him. 'Something's gone wrong with it. Frank will explain.'

Roger invited them both to sit down and Frank told them what the trouble was.

'It's not turning out the right shape. As soon as the first of the frames went in, I was suspicious, but as the design had been drawn by an expert I thought I must be mistaken. But now we're putting the planks in, I'm sure of it. The yacht just won't be stable.'

'And you're sure you've followed the measurements correctly?' asked Roger.

'Absolutely. Everything has been double checked. The figures are clear enough.'

Roger reached out for the telephone. 'There's only one thing to do. Get the designer here as soon as possible. In the meantime, find yourself some odd jobs around the yard.'

Within the hour the designer was at the boatyard. Together he and Roger, accompanied by Julia, went into the boat-building shed. The designer looked at the skeleton of the new yacht, then walked over to the wall where his design was pinned up.

'Do you mind if I take this into the light?' he asked.

'Of course not.'

The man removed the drawing pins and took the drawing out into the daylight. He studied it for a moment, then said emphatically:

'This isn't my drawing.'

Frank stared at him. 'But of course it's your drawing. When Mr Leighton gave it to me, I brought it straight into the shed and pinned it up.'

The designer shook his head. 'I don't care what you say. I didn't draw this. I've brought a photostat copy of the original with me in the car. I'll get it and you can compare the figures.'

'We'd better go to my office,' Roger said gravely.

There was no doubt about it. When the two drawings were compared they were identical in every particular except the measurements. At first glance they looked the same, but the figures showing dimensions were different.

'I don't know whose drawing *that* is,' the designer said, indicating the one Frank and his team had been working from, 'but it certainly isn't mine.'

'In that case, somebody or other has taken the one you supplied and substituted the other. Now who, I wonder, could it be?' Roger said grimly.

CHAPTER VIII

There was a silence in the office for a moment or two. No one, it seemed, was willing to speculate as to who was responsible. Frank Willis was the first to speak.

'Well, whoever the culprit is, one thing is certain. We shall have to begin all over again, so I'd best go and get on with it.' He glanced at Roger. 'I presume you want us to continue, Mr Leighton?'

'Of course. I only hope we can get to the bottom of this business.'

The designer rolled up the incorrect drawing. 'Just to make sure you start with the right one,' he said, 'I'll leave you with the photostat. And if I were you, I'd keep it under lock and key.'

'You bet,' answered Frank, going to the door. 'I shan't let it out of my sight.'

He went out and the designer turned to Roger. 'Shall I take this or do you want me to leave it with you?'

'Leave it,' Roger answered. 'I'll keep it locked up in my desk until I decide what to do about this business.'

When the designer had gone, Roger asked Julia: 'Have you any idea as to who might have monkeyed about with the design?'

Julia hesitated before answering. It would be a terrible thing to accuse anyone on mere suspicion.

'I'd—rather not say, Roger, if you don't mind. At least, not until I've had a little time to think.'

He nodded. 'Fair enough. I'll do a spot of thinking, too, then we can find out if we come up with the same answers.'

'But what good will it do? I think I'd rather not know who was responsible. Couldn't we just forget about it?'

His expression became stony. 'No, I don't think we can. At least, I can't. Until we find out, there'll be a continual suspicion surrounding everybody. It might even be one of our own workmen, and if it is, I just don't want the man working for me. It was done quite deliberately—and by someone who knew his way around as well as knowing what we were doing.'

'I realize that. That's why—'

The telephone rang and Roger lifted the receiver. The next moment his face became dark.

'It's for you,' he said. 'Max Windham. You'd better take it in your own office.'

Julia turned and went out. Why was it that nine times out of ten, when Max rang, Roger answered the telephone? But of course, that was nonsense and almost inevitable, no matter who rang, when they had only one line and an extension. She lifted the receiver of her own telephone and heard the click as Roger replaced his.

'Hello, Max.'

'Ah, darling girl,' came his cheerful voice. 'How are things?'

'"Things" are not too good,' she answered sharply, nettled at being called 'darling girl'.

'Oh?' he asked promptly. 'What's up?'

But almost immediately, she had regretted answering him the way she had.

'I'm sorry, it isn't something I can talk about.'

'Oh—mysterious. Well, what about a date?'

Julia suppressed a sigh. She didn't really want to see him, but she didn't want an argument and she certainly did not want Max to come to the houseboat again.

'Sorry, Max, I'm going to be tied up for the next few days.'

'Tied up where?' To your office desk?' he asked facetiously.

'I have things to do, anyway. So if you wouldn't mind—'

'What's the matter?' he persisted. 'Did I offend you the other evening?'

154

' No, of course you didn't. I just don't want to see you for a while, that's all. And I must ring off now, Max. 'Bye.'

As soon as she replaced the receiver Roger came through and passed outside without saying a word. Feeling utterly wretched, Julia sat down at her desk. Life really was becoming impossible. *Who* had stolen that design and replaced it with a false one? Tony Sheldrake was the first person who came into her mind. But from what motive? Annoyance at being given the sack? But he couldn't have acted so quickly. And how had the change-over been done? Frank would surely have noticed if the drawing had been missing at any time. She really couldn't see, in all honesty, how Tony Sheldrake *could* have been responsible. He had never been left alone in the boatyard, and Frank had discouraged any boatyard hands not concerned with the boatbuilding from going into the shed.

In a vague sort of way, as she went about her work, she went through the names of all the men who worked for Wingcraft, or who had any business in the yard, mentally eliminating them as most unlikely to do a thing like deliberately sabotage Roger's efforts.

But suddenly she was brought up with a jerk. Max. That Sunday morning when he had turned back to make a telephone call. Suppose he—

She rejected the idea, feeling ashamed of herself. It was true that he had tried to persuade herself to find various ways of ensuring that Roger did not succeed in the business. But that had been for her sake, so that Roger might become fed up and return to London, leaving her with another chance of becoming the owner herself. He had nothing to gain himself. Unlike Celia who—

This was terrible. She would be suspecting herself soon. That was the worst of trying to discover who had done a thing like this. Everybody was under suspicion. It would be far better to forget the whole incident. No

155

great harm had been done. It had put the project about a week behind and probably wasted a little timber, that was all.

Roger went about grim-faced. She saw him talking to one or other of the men throughout the day and guessed he was questioning them about the affair. But when it came to Tony Sheldrake's turn—whom Roger interviewed in the office, voices were raised very high indeed. It was impossible not to hear what they were saying.

'So now I'm being accused of spiriting away your precious boat design, and substituting a phoney one! Who did you blame for all these things before I came on the scene, I'd like to know?'

At first Roger's voice was quiet. 'I'm *not* accusing you. As to whom we blamed before you came, you force me to say that we *had* no troubles until recently. We never had engine troubles, for instance. And who is to blame for those sort of things if not the man whose job it is?'

'And because of a few lousy breakdowns I have to take the rap for everything? That's rich! Thank heaven I'm leaving tonight, that's all I can say!'

'But for the generosity of Miss Barclay you would have left weeks ago,' Roger answered. 'What I would like to know is—where were you, really, before you came here? And why did you choose this particular boatyard?'

Julia was about to go outside. This was tantamount to eavesdropping. But Sheldrake's next words arrested her.

'The generosity of Miss Barclay, indeed! Why don't you ask her if she knows anything about the yacht design? She's got the most to gain if you get so fed up that you quit, if all I hear is true.'

Now Roger's voice was thunderous. 'Get out of here, Sheldrake! Get out of here before I throw you out, and don't let me see you on these premises again. Your cards and your money will be posted to you. And don't be surprised if the police come knocking at your door!'

Sheldrake attempted to say something else, but the next moment the door was flung open by Roger.

'Out!' he roared, 'before I pick up the phone and send for the police to have you arrested!'

Sheldrake gave him a venomous look and glared at Julia as he stamped out.

Roger drew in an angry, tight-lipped breath. 'And how much of that did you hear?' he demanded of Julia.

'I'm sorry. All of it. I was going to go outside, but—'

'How I kept my hands off the man I'll never know. Get his cards out and make out a cheque for a week's wages for him. I'll sign it. And send it by registered post.'

He stamped out, and as she was looking in the filing cabinet for the man's insurance cards Julia saw Roger talking to Celia. What Sheldrake had said about herself was a terrible thing. Surely Roger had not taken the man seriously? It could so easily have been true. At least, some men might have thought so. He had made no effort to reassure her. She would have to ask him for his opinion.

But there was no opportunity that day of asking Roger anything. He and Celia went out sometime during the afternoon and did not return until quite late.

'Can I get you a drink?' Julia asked her. 'A cup of tea perhaps?' She had already learned that Celia did not like milky drinks. To her surprise Celia nodded.

'Yes, please,' she answered, and sat down. There was a brief silence while Julia switched on the kettle, then Celia announced: 'I'm going back home on Sunday. Roger's driving me, of course, and you might be interested to hear that I've promised to marry him.'

Everything within Julia tightened. 'Oh. Well, congratulations,' she answered stiffly, then forced herself to ask: 'Does that mean that Roger has agreed to go back to London to live?'

Celia nodded and smiled. 'This last upset about the design for the new yachts was the last straw. But I wouldn't mention it if I were you. He hates being fore-stalled. He'll tell you himself when he gets around to it. What he's going to do is put a really good man in charge. A manager, in other words. Then we shall come down here for week-ends and so on. So you see, I've won, after all. Roger wanted to come here for our honeymoon. I ask you! He's got some crazy notion of wanting to see the first of the new yachts finished. But a honeymoon here is out of the question. So we had to compromise, and the best that can be managed is a few days in Paris or somewhere, then a longer holiday, a sort of second honeymoon in October, maybe a winter cruise.'

'You're—planning to get married quite soon, then?'

'The sooner the better, so Roger says, and I agree with him. I shan't be working for the Melloid Oil Com-pany any more, of course. But I expect I shall have to work out my notice. The old man—Roger's father—will insist upon it. He's a perfect stinker to work for. I've only stuck it for as long as I have for Roger's sake.'

Julia did not comment. She excused herself and went into the small bathroom to have a shower and prepare for bed. For a little while a sort of mental defence mechanism made her think of all kinds of trivial things, things which had nothing to do with Roger, or at least, no bearing on what Celia had just told her. They were concerned with things like the weather, hoping it would be a fine day for tomorrow's change-over. There was nothing worse than a rainy Saturday. Naturally, the women who cleaned out the boats ready for the new hirers did not like coming and going through the rain—and after a wet week, the boats would be in a bad enough state as it was. Everything was made more difficult, and the new people arriving viewed the weather with a great deal of gloom, anxiety and apprehension.

And so until she finally lay down to sleep she thought of anything and everything except the subject closest to her heart. But even then her brain did not seem to function properly. She knew only one thing. Roger was going to marry Celia. He was in love with her.

The weather the following day was neither wet nor fine. It was cool, blustery and showery with now and then a sunny interval. With Tony Sheldrake gone, they were a hand short and his work was shared between Roger and Bob Winters, leaving the other engineer to continue working on the new craft, after all. Julia dealt with the business of clean linen for the craft, interviewed new arrivals, answered the telephone, handed out life-jackets and television sets, and when the need arose gave a helping hand to a novice. She avoided contact with Roger as much as possible, and he appeared to be avoiding her, too. They barely exchanged a word with each other all day. But when eventually the last of the boats had been sent on their way, he came into Julia's office.

'I understand Celia told you I'm driving her home tomorrow?'

'Yes,' she answered briefly.

'I have one or two things to attend to, so I shall stay over until Monday. I've asked Celia to be ready at nine-thirty in the morning. Would you mind seeing that she's up in time and has some breakfast?'

'Of course.' Had Celia been complaining about having no breakfast? 'At least,' she amended, 'I'll *try* to get her to eat something. She doesn't eat much breakfast.'

'I know, but going on a journey is different, and I don't want to have to make too many stops. One for lunch will be sufficient if we can find somewhere.'

Julia suggested Baldock, and he thanked her, then went out. Celia spent the evening with him in the house, and Julia a lonely one in the houseboat. For the first time, while she was eating her solitary meal, she tried to think rationally, decide what to do. If Roger married Celia before the season was over and they spent the rest of the summer here as man and wife, even if only at week-ends, then it would be impossible for herself to stay here. If he did not tell her quite soon what his plans were, she would simply have to ask him. She must talk to him also about the switch of the drawing for the new yachts. She felt certain that she was under suspicion, otherwise why had he been avoiding her all day? He had not said whether he was pursuing his enquiries or calling in the police or anything. It hurt her terribly to think that he was giving even a second thought to the idea that she would do anything to harm him, or considered her remotely capable of such a mean action. As soon as he came back from London she must have a talk with him, she decided. If he were going to take on a manager eventually, there was no reason why he should not begin to advertise almost immediately, and as soon as he found someone she could leave.

For a little while she found her loneliness and unhappiness almost unbearable. She went outside, feeling like making her escape then and there. Why hadn't she done something about getting another car? She must. She would need one soon anyway if she were going home. She hated travelling long distances by train.

Frank Willis was still in the boat-building shed. Feeling that if she didn't talk to someone she would go crazy, she opened the door.

He looked up as she entered. 'How's it going now, Frank?' she asked.

'Fine now, miss, but I'm not taking any chances. In future this drawing goes with me when I leave the boatyard.'

'I—suppose that's a good idea, but you don't think it's rather like bolting the door after the horse has gone?'

He glanced at her sharply. 'What do you mean by that, Miss Barclay?'

'Why, nothing,' she answered quickly. 'It's just a

saying. All the same, I can't think that any of the men we've got now—' She broke off in some confusion. She was as good as accusing Tony Sheldrake to Frank. It was all wrong.

But he took her up. 'You're saying in so many words that Sheldrake knew something about it, aren't you?'

'Well, I—'

'If you didn't trust him I wonder you took him on,' he said sharply.

Julia's eyes widened. Frank Willis had never spoken to her that way before. Never. Deciding not to continue the discussion, she went out. Already, it seemed, the business of the drawing was causing rifts between people. She had the horrible feeling just now that Frank was in effect blaming her. Her decision to leave as soon as possible was strengthened.

Celia did not stay late with Roger. Julia supposed he had suggested an early night because of making a good start in the morning.

'Would you like me to help you pack tonight?' Julia asked her. 'It would save an awful lot of time in the morning.'

But Celia refused. 'I can't think why Roger wants to make such an early start. I don't like having my clothes packed all night. I shall do it in the morning. You can help me then if you like—and he will just have to wait until I'm ready. Roger can be very domineering, and when he's domineering he's a bore.'

Julia sighed worriedly. She couldn't see how they were possibly going to be happy if Celia kept up this kind of behaviour.

'I—fail to see how you could ever think of Roger as a bore,' she told the other girl.

Celia laughed shortly. 'You need to take off those rose-coloured spectacles of yours. It's far better to marry a man knowing his faults than to imagine he's perfect and discover all of them afterwards.'

' I suppose so.'

It sounded logical, but Julia was not convinced. She did not want to continue the conversation however, so she said no more. Later, she thought to herself that though she might often be angry with Roger, she would never, never find him boring.

She set her alarm so that she would make sure of not oversleeping, and after some tossing about, fell into an uneasy sleep.

Celia did not keep Roger waiting very long the following morning after all, and with her departure Julia heaved a sigh of relief. It was very nice indeed to have the place to herself. She decided that a degree of loneliness was preferable to the wrong kind of company. In any case she had still had times of loneliness even when Celia had been here. Loneliness was not the same thing as being alone.

Frank Willis and his team had decided to work that Sunday until about four o'clock. One of them promised to keep an eye on the boatyard in general, so when she had put her own clothes back in the small wardrobe, and the houseboat was looking more normal, Julia took the van out with the idea of calling at a garage she knew which always had one or two second-hand cars for sale. There were several in her price range standing in the garage yard, and after she had had a trial run in them, she chose one in pale grey with wine-coloured upholstery.

' How soon can I have it?' she asked Jack Parker, the young proprietor.

' Oh, it shouldn't take more than a few days to get the log book changed over. It's taxed to the end of the month. In fact, if you're wanting to use it, I can run it along for you in the morning.

She was able to pay cash, so there was no problem about hire purchase, and though she did not know a great deal about engines, she could detect no faults or hear any peculiar noises when she had been on the trial run. Jack assured her that it had been well overhauled and had passed the Ministry of Transport test.

'Anyway,' was his final word, 'use it for a little while and if you do find anything wrong, bring it along and I'll put it right. Okay?'

She agreed, knowing she could trust him to keep his word and he said he would deliver it the following morning. He couldn't leave the garage that day, as he was on his own.

She returned to the boatyard, and for the rest of the day time dragged. A couple of day boats had been taken out on hire, but that was all, and when those had been brought in again, there was nothing for her to do except potter around the houseboat until bedtime.

Roger returned about four o'clock on Monday afternoon. 'Hello, what's this?' he enquired, seeing her new car standing outside the houseboat.

'It's mine. I bought it yesterday,' she told him.

'Have you got the log book?' he asked, giving a keen look at the bodywork and tyres.

'Not yet. But it's taxed up to the end of the month.'

'You've given it a trial run, I suppose?'

'Oh yes.'

'Mm. Looks all right. As a matter of interest, how much did you pay for it?' She told him and he said she had a good bargain. 'Provided you don't have any troubles when you've run it for a bit.'

The short week-end seemed to have done him good, she thought. He was certainly more cheerful. Perhaps he had decided to forget about the business of the yacht design after all. That had certainly cast a blight over everything and everyone. Or was his changed mood due to the fact that Celia had promised to marry him?

Some days passed and she waited for him to tell her of his plans, that he was going back to work for his father, but he didn't. She longed to ask him. Not that she wanted confirmation of his engagement, but the suspense was becoming more than she could bear. She avoided contact with him, and at every opportunity took out the new car so that she could familiarize herself with the gear changes, which were different both from her last car and the firm's van, as well as to make sure that it was in good running order. Now and again Roger would eye her keenly, then one evening he said, as she was putting the cover on her typewriter:

' How's the car running?'

' Fine,' she answered.

' Are you going out tonight?'

' I—don't know. I hadn't thought about it.'

There was a slight pause, then he said: ' I was wondering if you'd care to come over to the house, maybe play the piano, and we could have a coffee or something.'

She shook her head swiftly. It would be more than she could take, to be alone with him for any length of time in such an intimate atmosphere. Whether he told her soon of his plans or not, she must get away.

' I won't, if you don't mind,' she answered. ' But I'd like to have a word with you in the morning, if I may.'

His jaw tightened. He was annoyed at her refusal, of course. ' I shall be here,' he said coolly, and walked out.

She felt miserable for the rest of the evening, and wished once or twice that she had not been so much of a coward. Possibly he was missing Celia. She should have been willing to spend the evening with him for his sake. The house, it seemed, was all finished now. He would undoubtedly have shown her the upstairs rooms, and she decided once again that it would have been more than she could bear.

She slept little that night, not looking forward to her interview with him. But towards the middle of the morning she tapped at his office door and went in.

' Is it convenient to speak to you now?' she asked.

He glanced up from a letter he was reading and from across the desk she recognized Celia's writing.

He indicated a chair. ' Now, what's it all about?' he

asked.

Now that it came to the point she hardly knew how to begin. ' Well, I—it's—it's like this,' she began, then hesitated.

He picked up a pencil and began to doodle. She watched, fascinated as a head began to take shape. Then he glanced up swiftly and she shifted her gaze uncomfortably.

He screwed up the sheet of paper just as he had on that other morning. It was Celia's head he was drawing, of course.

' What's the trouble?' he prompted.

' Well, I—' she began again. Then in a rush: ' I'm sorry, Roger, but I've come to tell you that I'm leaving.'

His eyes widened and he stared at her for a moment or two, then his expression became cold. He began drawing again.

' What made you change your mind?' he asked without looking up.

' Change my mind?' she queried.

He glanced up then. ' Yes. When I first bought Wingcraft you had been all set to buy the business yourself—couldn't bear to tear yourself away. Maybe it would make a difference to you if I told you I was thinking of getting out.'

Her heart leapt uncomfortably. ' Are you?' she asked jerkily.

' You'd be happier if I wasn't here, wouldn't you?'

She felt herself colouring. Had he guessed how she felt about him?

He bent to his doodle again and she tried to keep her eyes from following the lines of his pencil.

' Yes,' he continued. ' You want Wingcraft—but without having me around. As a matter of fact, I've been thinking of offering you a partnership.'

' A—a partnership?' she echoed.

' That's right.' He stopped doodling and sat back in his chair and gave her a long look. ' A sort of working

165

partner. It's fair enough. I go back to the family business—or I might do something else—you stay here and manage the place, and we share the profits. How would that suit you?'

She stared at him. ' It—sounds extremely generous, but I'm—not sure that it would work. You'd—still come back from time to time, wouldn't you?'

She avoided mentioning Celia. After all, he had not told her yet of his intention to marry her.

He did not answer for a moment, then he said quietly: ' Does the idea horrify you so much? I had no idea you were all that anxious to be rid of me.'

' But I'm not—' she began hotly, then checked herself. ' It's just that—' She sighed and broke off again. She could hardly say: *It isn't you I don't want to see, it's your wife.* Or: *I couldn't bear it because I love you so much.* ' I think I *will* leave, if you don't mind. It would be the best. My father can always use help in the orchards.'

Roger regarded her for a minute. ' Is that what you *really* want to do? I thought you were still in love with —the boatyard and Norfolk. Don't you want to see the new auxiliaries finished?'

' It would have been nice, yes, but—'

He flung down his pencil. ' Look, why not sleep on it for a little while longer? I think I've just about had enough of the boat-hire business, anyway. We can work out something. I'll see you again in the morning.'

He picked up the telephone and began to dial a number, so Julia had no alternative but to go back to her own office.

A partnership. The only partnership she would ever want with Roger was that of his— She could not say the word wife even in her thoughts. It was too painful. And what difference would it make to the situation if she were a business partner? He would still pay visits to the place and bring Celia to stay. He had said nothing about selling the house. Why should he? But the very fact of his talking about going back to the oil business or something else confirmed what Celia had said—if confirmation were needed. There was no reason at all why she should have told a pack of lies.

During the afternoon Max rang her. She had neither heard from him or seen him since the night he had had a meal with her in the boathouse, the night she and Roger had had the talk in the darkened boatyard. But she did not want to think about that.

'Seems ages since I've seen you,' Max was saying. 'What about tonight?'

She did not really want to see him, on the other hand the thought of another evening alone in the houseboat almost caused her to groan aloud.

'All right, Max, thanks. But don't come to the boat-yard. I'll meet you in town.'

He agreed without question, and they arranged to meet at a certain restaurant. When next she saw Roger, she mentioned she would be going out that evening.

'Not alone?' he queried.

She shook her head. 'With Max. But don't worry, he won't be coming to the boatyard.'

He frowned for a moment, then obviously remembered what he had said the last time Max was here.

'You'd better forget that,' he said shortly, and strode over to the house. Julia looked at his back and knew that she could not stand this for much longer. She could not get away that evening soon enough, and consequently was at the meeting place five minutes earlier than Max.

'I'm not late, am I?' he asked.

'No, no, I'm early.'

Max said little of any consequence until they had almost finished their meal, then he said soberly:

'What's been happening at your place, Julia? I saw Tony Sheldrake the other day and he was mighty sore. I understand he had a row with Leighton.'

'Well, yes, he did, but he was leaving in any case. Did he tell you what the "row" was about?'

Max nodded. 'Something about the sketch plan of the new auxiliaries Frank Willis was working on.'

'That's right.'

As he already knew something about it, Julia could see no harm in filling in the details. It helped to be able to talk anyhow.

'So what is Leighton doing about it now?' Max queried when she had told him what had happened.

Julia shook her head. 'I don't know. He seems to be letting the matter drop. In fact, he's—thinking of going back to London.'

Max's eyes opened wide. 'No! Really?'

Julia eyed him with an ironic smile. 'I expect that pleases you.'

Max pursed his lips. 'We-ll, it's no use my being hypocritical about it, is it? I had an idea he'd get fed up before long. But what about you? Are you going to buy the business, after all?'

'I don't think he wants to sell. As a matter of fact, he's offered me a partnership.'

'A partnership?' Max echoed. 'Good lord! That's one thing I didn't think of. I mean—'

'Neither did I. Celia said he was going to hire a manager. But he must have done some further thinking. He—doesn't want me to put any capital in, just leave me to do the managing on a profit-sharing basis.'

'Oh.' Max seemed at a loss for words for a moment. Then he said suddenly: 'Did you accept—or haven't you made up your mind yet?'

'I'm seeing him about it in the morning. But I shan't accept. I want to get away.'

Max played with his fork thoughtfully. 'I shall be sorry to see you go and I shall miss you, of course, but I think you're doing the wisest thing really. In my opinion the heyday of the Broads holiday industry has been reached and will probably decline when the new regulations about sewage are in force. It will be precious little use building new craft unless new toilet arrangements are made, and the cost of converting those already in existence will be something to be reckoned with.'

Julia had heard vaguely about these new regulations, but the whole subject had been dropped for quite a while, and she—among plenty of others, she suspected—had forgotten all about it for the time being.

'Oh dear. The regulations really are coming about, are they?'

Max nodded. 'I got the news from a friend of mine on the River Board. It will be in all the papers in a day or two's time.'

Julia frowned, thinking of the possible effect on Roger. But she said optimistically: 'I expect the boat-owners' associations will get together and devise some method. There has to be some way round the problem without altering the design of all the boats.'

'Well, whatever they do, it's almost bound to put the hire price up, and between ourselves prices are quite high enough already. *Too* high, in some case. In fact the thin end of the wedge is already showing. For the first time in years one of the boatyards were advertising in the local paper today that they had boats available for hire. Normally, just about every boat in existence is booked up the previous year. Some of these fellows —my own father included—have just about expanded themselves out of business. It was bound to happen.'

Expanded themselves out of business. Was that what Roger would do eventually? She must have a talk with him in the morning, warn him, even though she couldn't help feeling that Max was being somewhat pessimistic. The Broads offered just the kind of holiday people needed today, and were seeking. One of complete relaxation in which they could unwind. It was the effect of gliding smoothly along, miles away, or seemingly, from the rush of road traffic, of being able to look deep into the reflections on the water, to watch lazily the tall reeds bending to the breeze, or moor in some quiet spot and sunbathe or fish, and in the evenings either find entertainment ashore or settle down to an evening's television.

'Roger isn't planning to build any more large luxury cruisers anyway,' she said, more or less speaking her thoughts aloud. 'And I think those are the main reasons for the Broads having reached saturation point.'

'You could be right, but it's all a matter of conjecture,' answered Max. 'Some people blame the weather and the cheap package holidays abroad, but these new regulations are going to be the death knell.'

'I hope not,' murmured Julia. 'Otherwise there are going to be a lot of people out of work.'

But she was thinking mainly of Roger and beginning to feel guilty about leaving the business.

'By the way,' Max said casually, 'talking of people being out of work, did I ever tell you—Tony Sheldrake worked at our place at one time?'

Julia stared at him in astonishment. 'No, you didn't tell me, and I find it rather odd.'

'Oh, sorry. I thought I had. But I can't see that it matters.'

'But he didn't give me any references from your firm,' Julia protested.

'No? Well, maybe he had enough without ours.'

'Maybe. Will you take him on again?'

'I don't know. We might, I suppose, if he comes and asks us. We've got so many cruisers, we could always do with an extra engineering hand. Actually, we found him pretty good. I reckon he had a run of bad luck at your place.'

Julia was about to ask Max why Sheldrake had left them in that case, but Max began talking about something else, and it didn't seem very important. Soon it was time to put an end to the evening, and Max walked with her to the car park.

As she drove to the boatyard Julia wondered if prospects in the Broads holiday business were as grim as Max had painted them. There would be, undoubtedly, a curb on the number of new craft built. At least, for a year or two, but she felt that would not be a bad thing at all. And Roger's plans for expansion? After he had built the first of the new auxiliaries, perhaps he would soft-pedal. But now she was worried about the idea of leaving and going back home. Ought she to stay and manage the place for him, accept his offer of a partnership? Then she told herself she simply couldn't. It had been bad enough while Celia had been here on holiday, but as Roger's wife—

Roger was late coming into the office the next morning, and when he did she was startled at the look of anger on his face.

'Is—anything wrong?' she asked him.

'Wrong?' he echoed coldly. 'Yes, there is. Did you know that that Sheldrake fellow was one of Windham's men?'

Julia's stomach muscles contracted violently. 'Why —yes, I did, but—'

His eyes blazed. 'Well, that's rich, I must say! You and Windham concocted a nice little plan between you, didn't you? And now you've got what you wanted. Me out of the way. Or will have in a very short space of time, I can tell you. Because I've just about had enough!'

He stormed into his office and slammed the door. Julia stared at it, then got slowly to her feet.

CHAPTER IX

Julia was halfway to Norwich before she realized what she had done. She slowed down and looked for somewhere to pull in so that she could collect her thoughts.

When Roger had gone into his office, she had only one thought in her mind. To get away. To get—anywhere away from Roger and the boatyard. Without stopping to think of what she was doing or where she was going she had jumped into her car and automatically turned towards Norwich.

She drew into a quiet side street and stopped the car. Running away, that's what she had been doing. But hadn't she taken as much as any human being could, or should? Roger obviously thought the worst of her. He had accused her, *actually accused her*—of being in league with Max and Sheldrake to cause trouble for him so that he would become fed up enough to leave. He thought she had known from the beginning that Sheldrake once worked for Windhams. How could he? How could he possibly suggest such a thing? But he had. And it was unthinkable that she should stay in his employ a moment longer.

Her hand reached out to the ignition. She would go home. He wouldn't want her at the boatyard any longer, anyhow. She would go home and telephone him from there. Mrs Harris would pack her belongings and send them on if she wrote and asked her. There was only one problem. She had not enough petrol to get her all the way to Kent and she had no money. She had not even stopped to pick up her handbag or anything. But there was an engineering firm in Norwich with whom Wingcraft had an account. They knew her well. She would ask them to fill up her tank and put it on the firm's account, then pay Roger later. With regard to food, she would just have to go hungry until she arrived home.

Anger dulled the pain in her heart, and once she had a tank full of petrol, with a spare gallon in a can she always carried, she drove with fierce concentration, stopping only once for a brief rest. Surely Max hadn't had anything to do with the stealing of the yacht design? Max and Sheldrake between them?

Snatches of conversation with Max kept coming back to her. He had wanted her to try to make Roger give up, or at any rate to be unco-operative with that end. It had been no less a shock to her than to Roger to discover that Sheldrake had worked at Windham's. Could Max have sent him to deliberately sabotage the business? She asked herself with what object. Not on her behalf, surely? She had given him plainly to understand that she did not want the business and would do nothing against Roger.

As her mind went over one probability after another, recalling some of the things Max had said from time to time, it occurred to her how fed up Max had been with working for his father. Was it possible that Max wanted to buy Wingcraft himself? But she dismissed this idea. If he'd wanted it he could have bid for it when she herself withdrew. Unless—unless the price was too high, and he hoped that, by making things difficult for Roger, he might get the business cheaper. But he had never at any time mentioned that he would like his own boat-hire business.

She sighed and tried to dismiss the whole matter from her mind. Only one thing mattered. Roger thought her capable of working against him. That coupled with the fact that she loved him and he was going to marry someone else reduced everything else to unimportance.

When she arrived home she was at the point of exhaustion with hunger and fatigue, coupled with emotional upset.

'Darling, what a lovely surprise!' her mother ex-

173

claimed when she pushed open the kitchen door. Then, as she looked at her face, ' But something's wrong, isn't it? You look—upset, as well as tired. Come into the sitting room.'

Julia practically collapsed into a chair. ' Oh, thank goodness I'm home!'

' When did you last eat, young lady?' her mother asked, eyeing her keenly.

Julia leaned back wearily. ' Oh, I—didn't stop for anything to eat. I wanted to get home. I'm all right, Mother, really, but a cup of tea would be nice.'

' You need more than a cup of tea, by the look of you,' Mrs Barclay said firmly. ' Stay right there and I'll bring you something in.'

She went out and Julia closed her eyes. As soon as she had eaten she would ring Roger. Or better still, ask her mother to ring him. Her mother would think it odd and there were bound to be questions to answer, but nothing would induce her to go back to Norwich.

Within a few minutes her mother came in with some tea and poured a cup out for her.

' Drink this while you're waiting. It'll put a bit of life into you, at any rate.'

It did. Julia sipped it thankfully. In a very short time later Mrs Barclay returned with cold meat and salad, brown bread and butter and a jar of honey.

' Thanks, Mum. I feel better already,' said Julia, slipping back to her childhood name for her mother.

Helen Barclay smiled, and as Julia ate, she talked about the orchards, her husband, and local news in general. Then as Julia sat back with another cup of tea, she said :

' And now what's your news? Tell me why you were in such a hurry to come home you didn't even stop to pack a case or even bring your handbag.'

Julia gave a thin smile. ' It's no use trying to hide anything from you, Mum, is it?'

Her mother raised her eyebrows. ' Well, my dear,

that much is pretty obvious, so come on, out with it.'

It wasn't easy to know how to start. 'I know you'll think I'm pretty silly, and maybe that I've behaved rather badly, but really I had no option,' she began.

'No option but to do what? You'd better tell me.'

As briefly as she could Julia told her mother about the hiring of Tony Sheldrake by herself, about the engine troubles, the switch of the drawings, her conversation with Max the previous evening and so to the scene this morning.

Helen Barclay frowned. 'And, darling, you walked out and drove off without giving him time to cool down or anything?'

Anger was slowly ebbing away to expose pain and heartbreak. 'I—I just couldn't take any more, Mother. You see, I—I'm in love with him and—'

She compressed her lips and tried to hold back her tears, but it was no use. They spilled over, and for a few minutes sobs of despair shook her. Her mother took away the tray and the tea things, then put her arm around Julia's shoulders.

'Look, darling, go and lie down for a bit, then we'll talk again later. I'm sure there's a way through this.'

But Julia shook her head vigorously. 'No, Mother. It isn't just this morning's episode. He's in love with Celia—the girl I told you about in my letter. I could never go back, and there's little point in talking. I'd just rather forget all about—everything as quickly as possible. There's only one thing. As he doesn't know where I am, will you give him a ring and let him know? Tell him I'll write to him in a day or so, that I'm sorry to inconvenience him by leaving so suddenly, but—but that I'm sure he'll understand.'

'Yes, dear, all right. I'll tell him. Now off you go to your room and try to sleep. You must be exhausted.'

Upstairs, Julia washed her face, then took off her dress and slid under the counterpane. Thoroughly spent now with weeping and the long journey, she closed her eyes and fell into a sleep of exhaustion and did not waken until her mother came into the room to tell her that the evening meal would be ready in five minutes.

'I came up earlier, but you were sound asleep. Here, drink this. It will help you to wake up. I couldn't let you stay any longer, otherwise you'd never sleep tonight.'

Julia sat up and her mother put another cup of tea into her hands.

'Did you—ring Roger, Mother?' she asked.

'Ye-es, I did.'

'What did he say?'

'Well, he'd been worried about you, of course. He also said that he'd lost his temper and was sorry. He was very relieved when I told him you were at home and wanted to speak to you, but I told him you were resting.'

'Did he ask when I was going back?'

'No, dear, he didn't. I told him you'd said you were going to write to him and he said he'd look forward to hearing from you. Now, your father's home, so drink up and put on something pretty and come down to dinner.'

'What did you tell Father?' she asked.

'More or less what you told me, dear, and he thinks as I do—that it was a misunderstanding, and it will all get sorted out.'

Julia felt like screaming. 'But, Mother, it *won't* " all get sorted out ". All right, so Roger was annoyed, he blew his top and now he's sorry. But that isn't important. It's—it's the other thing. I had to get away and I'm not going back. If Father hasn't a job for me in the orchards—'

'Now, now, Julia darling, that's quite enough,' her mother said firmly. 'You know perfectly well there'll always be a job in the orchards if you want one.'

Julia compressed her lips. 'I'm sorry, Mother. But I'm afraid you still don't quite understand.'

Helen Barclay took the cup from her hands and sat on the bed, putting her arm round Julia's shoulders.

'I think I do, darling, but if I don't then we must talk some more and you must make me understand. Now come along, your father's longing to see you and he's waiting for his dinner—which will be ruined if I don't go down and attend to it.'

Julia smiled, ashamed of her outburst. 'I won't be long—and thanks for the tea. It was lovely.'

She had a shower and dressed quickly. She had the best and most understanding parents in the world, but she mustn't burden them with her troubles. She would just have to learn to forget Roger. It was the only thing to do.

Her father greeted her with a big hug. 'I see you've bought yourself another car,' he said almost immediately. 'Looks a nice little job. And you had no mechanical troubles on the journey?'

Julia blessed him for not asking questions about the circumstances of her coming.

'No troubles at all,' she told him. 'And how's the fruit industry? Is it going to be a good harvest?'

He crossed his fingers. 'So far, so good. One thing about a wet spring—you don't get those killer morning frosts.'

It was almost as though she had never been away—except for the dull ache deep inside her which she tried to ignore. She talked shop with her father, and local news and generalities with her mother. But when they were drinking their nightcap, she found herself saying suddenly:

'Father, do you think I acted badly in just walking out and coming home without a word? Do you think I should have—'

Her father shook his head and put his hand on hers. 'My dear, we all of us do hasty things at times. If we were perfect we wouldn't be human. You acted on impulse, that's all. You didn't behave badly deliber-

177

ately. It wasn't calculated. You had obviously reached the end of your endurance about one thing and another, and the first place you thought of was home, that's all.'

Tears gathered in her throat. She smiled her thanks through a mist of tears.

' But I should have had more character, more—powers of endurance. It was just plain selfish to run away like that.'

Tom Barclay filled his pipe and lit it. ' We could all do with more of those things, so I think you'd better stop blaming yourself and tell us a little more about it, especially if it's going to make you sleep any better.'

Julia leaned back in her chair. ' The crux of the whole matter is, Father, I'm in love with Roger—but he isn't with me.'

' Well, you're by no means the first person to run away from a situation like that,' commented her father. ' But what makes you think he isn't in love with you?'

Julia stared at him. ' Wouldn't he have said so, or have found some way of letting me know it? Besides—'

She told him about Celia, and all the little things which were evidence enough without what Celia had told her in addition.

' And has he told you his plans himself?' queried her father.

' Some of them. He's going back to London, just as Celia said. In fact, he offered me a partnership. A sort of working partnership on a profit-sharing basis. But he'd be coming down—to the boatyard, I mean—for week-ends and holidays, and bringing Celia—'

' As his wife. And that's what you couldn't stand,' finished her father for her. ' And I don't blame you in the least. I suppose Roger hasn't got the least idea how you feel about him?'

' Of course not. I couldn't possibly—'

' Tom,' his wife said in a remonstrative tone, ' a girl

has her pride.'

'So has a man,' he answered swiftly. 'For one thing, what about this Max fellow you've been seeing? It's possible Roger thinks you're in love with him.'

Julia shook her head. 'He knows I'm not. I told him myself I wasn't all that keen on Max.'

'You did? Oh.' Tom Barclay puffed on his pipe. 'I must say I liked Roger Leighton. I wonder what he'll do about the boatyard now?'

'I don't know,' Julia answered with a sigh. 'Put a manager in charge, I suppose.'

'You don't think he'll sell it?'

'I don't know,' she said again. 'I hope not.' She felt sure he wouldn't sell to Max in any case. But Max could still have it one day by buying it from someone else.

'Why do you hope not?' pursued her father.

She frowned. 'I—suppose because of its associations with David. That's why I wanted to buy it, if you remember. I couldn't bear the idea of anyone else having it. Of course once I got to know Roger—'

Tom Barclay nodded thoughtfully, but said no more, and a short time after that they all went to bed.

The following day Julia wrote two letters. One to Mrs Harris, asking her to pack her clothes and send them on, and the other to Roger. The one to Mrs Harris was easy to write, but when it came to Roger's, she tore up first one, then the other.

In the end she wrote a brief formal letter apologizing for leaving so abruptly and told him to keep her month's salary, which was due, in lieu of notice. She signed her name, then after a moment's indecision, added the postscript: *I wish you and Celia every happiness*.

She despatched it by first-class mail, and subconsciously waited anxiously for his reply. But the week passed and she did not receive one. A registered letter came from Mrs Harris containing the money which had been in her purse, her cheque book and several letters.

179

A parcel followed in which was packed her handbag and one or two other small items. The rest was to follow by rail. She stopped asking her mother: 'Any post for me?' and busied herself in her father's office and helping to keep an eye on the fruit trees. But somehow she could not settle. She felt restless, as though she was not where she should be, yet she shrank from the thought of ever going back to the boatyard, even if Roger wanted her to now.

On Sunday afternoon she was alone in the house. Her mother and father had gone out to keep an engagement they had made prior to Julia coming home.

'You won't be going out, will you, darling?' asked her mother as Julia saw them to their car.

'I wasn't thinking of doing so,' she answered. 'Why?'

'I'm rather expecting someone to call. Someone I couldn't very well put off.'

'But who—' she began through the open window of the car.

Her father pulled the starter. 'If we don't get off we shall be late.'

Her mother's next words were drowned by the roar of the accelerator, and the car made off down the drive in a cloud of dust.

The house seemed strangely quiet. Julia wandered from room to room and found her thoughts straying to the boatyard, wondering how the work on the new auxiliaries was getting along, wishing she could go for a sail, wondering what Roger was doing. She had been wrong to leave. She knew that now. But it was too late. Feeling miserable and unhappy beyond belief she sat down at the piano, but as she played she was thinking of Roger's house, playing his piano while he was in the kitchen making coffee and listening to her play.

The ringing of the front door bell brought her to her senses with a painful jolt. This would be the caller her mother was expecting. She opened the door, then her eyes widened and she drew in a swift breath.

'Roger! What—what on earth are you doing here?'

He eyed her uncertainly. 'I've brought your things. It seemed—better than sending them by rail.'

'Oh, I see. That's very kind of you. Thank you very much.'

His lips curved into a slight smile. 'There was another reason for my coming. Do you think I could come in and talk to you for a moment?'

She suddenly realized she was keeping him standing on the doorstep.

'I'm sorry. Do come in, of course. I'm afraid Mother and Father aren't in at the moment. If they'd known—'

He stepped inside. 'That's all right. Perhaps they'll be back soon, anyway.'

She led him into the sitting room. 'Would you like some tea?' she asked.

He sat down. 'I think I'd rather talk first, if you don't mind. I should have answered your letter, but I thought it better to—come and see you.'

'Why didn't you let me know you were coming? I might have been out. In fact, if Mother hadn't said she was expecting someone to call—'

'Your letter was so—formal, I thought you must still be angry and might not want to see me,' he told her with a speculative glance.

She did not answer. Surely he had not come all this way just for a chat with her? But of course not. He had almost certainly been coming to see Celia and had thought he might as well drop in to have a talk about things. But she did not want any recriminations. They had both apologized, so—

'*Are* you pleased to see me, Julia?' he asked quizzically.

She didn't know how to answer him. 'I—just don't see what we've got to say to each other, Roger.'

'You don't? You mean you're quite content to let all these misunderstandings remain between us for ever?'

'I don't know what misunderstandings you mean,' she answered without looking at him. 'If you really believe that I'd plot against you to get rid of you, there's no more to be said.'

'I *don't* believe it,' he said with quiet emphasis.

'But you suspected me,' she flashed back at him.

He shook his head. 'I didn't, Julia. Not seriously. But if you remember, I *did* ask you if you knew Sheldrake worked for Max Windham and you said yes.'

'You didn't give me a chance to finish,' she said angrily. 'I was going to tell you that I didn't know until the previous evening. In any case—'

'Did Windham tell you he intended to make me an offer for Wingcraft?' he asked.

She gave him a startled look. 'No. No, he didn't. You didn't accept his offer?'

'Would it matter to you?'

She clasped her hands together and lowered her head. 'Yes. Yes, it would. I wouldn't want Max to have it.'

'I suspect that you don't want anyone to have it,' he told her quietly. 'Am I right?'

'I—I don't know.'

She couldn't quite explain even to herself how she felt about the boatyard. Ownership for David's sake had ceased to matter when she had fallen in love with Roger. Now she could not visualize anyone there but Roger.

He kept his gaze on her face. 'Would you reconsider my offer of partnership?'

Julia leaned back in her chair and closed her eyes momentarily.

'Roger, please go away. I've told you—'

He stood up, his face taut. 'All right, I'll go. I was something of a fool to come. You've disliked me right from the start, haven't you?'

She stared at him. How could a man be so blind?
'If—if I'd disliked you all that much, I wouldn't have
agreed to work for you.'

He turned away from her. 'Are you sure you didn't
merely tolerate me because you just couldn't bear to
leave the place?'

For a moment she did not answer. Feeling near to
tears, she looked at his back as he gazed out of the
window, and a feeling of infinite tenderness swept over
her. Her pride slowly ebbed away.

'No, Roger, I *didn't* merely tolerate you.'

He swung round. 'Then why is the idea of a partnership so—so repugnant to you?

'It's—not repugnant, Roger, it's—' She broke off.
How could she possibly tell him?

He caught her expression and came swiftly to her side,
bringing his chair close up to hers.

'I—mustn't go away without saying what I came to
say. The—sort of partnership I had in mind was
different from the one I put to you before. I want a
different kind of partnership altogether.'

'You—mean you'd stay and work along with me, not
go back to London?'

'Something like that.'

'So Celia has changed her mind about living in
Norfolk.'

'Celia?' he echoed in a puzzled voice. 'Oh yes, that
reminds me, what did you mean by that postscript to
your letter?'

She frowned. 'What should it mean except what it
said? I—just wished you both every happiness, that's
all.'

'But why? Are you under the impression that she
and I are going to be married or something?'

'Why, yes. Aren't you?'

He shook his head slowly. 'Where'd you get the
idea?'

'From—from Celia.'

183

'She actually said so, did she?' he persisted.

'Yes. Surely it was true. I mean—'

'Surely it wasn't,' he answered in a decisive tone. He took both her hands in his. 'I never even asked her. How could I when it was you I wanted?'

Her heart gave a tremendous leap. 'Roger! Roger, you don't mean that.'

'I most certainly do. But I was willing to—more or less let you have the boatyard, if that was what you wanted.'

She shook her head swiftly and her eyes misted over. 'I don't want it, not without you,' she told him tremulously.

His grip on her hands tightened. He gave a tremendous sigh and cupped her face in his hands.

'Julia! Oh, Julia, say that again and keep on saying it.'

She blinked. 'Tell me more about that partnership.'

He looked at her with an expression of infinite tenderness. 'It's a sort of life partnership,' he said softly. 'You know the kind of thing. There's a ceremony to which we invite all our friends. We make promises to love and honour and to cling only to each other until death us do part. I slip a plain gold ring on your finger, we sign our names in a book, then live happily ever after. Together, of course,' he added.

'I—I think I'd like that,' she whispered.

He gave her a long look, then brought his lips down on hers in a lingering kiss which sent her floating on a cloud of exquisite happiness.

'Do you love me, Julia?' he asked, searching her face.

She gave a little smile. 'Need you ask?'

'Yes, and I need to be told. In fact there are one or two things which need clearing up before we go any further.' He pulled her to her feet. 'Come and sit beside me and let's talk a little.'

They sat on the long settee and he put his arm around

her. ' I love you, Julia. I just want to be sure that there will never be any ghosts between us.'

' Ghosts?' she queried, running her fingers down his cheek.

He nodded. ' I realized quite early on that I'd nothing to fear from Max Windham. You were not in love with him, and never could be. I had a much more serious rival.'

' You mean—'

' I mean David. He was the reason for your wanting to buy the business, wasn't he? You couldn't bear the thought of anyone else taking his place. I thought you might gradually recover from that, but instead it seemed to get worse. You kept talking about going away. The very mention of his name caused you pain. I love you, Julia, and I want to marry you, but I couldn't bear it if I thought you were still in love with somebody else, that every time you looked at me or saw me around the place you were wishing I was another man.'

She turned to face him and put her arms about his neck. ' Darling Roger, it's you I love—and only you. I *was* in love with David. Of course I was. But that was nothing compared with what I feel for you. It's— true that I wanted to buy Wingcraft because I couldn't bear the thought of a stranger having it, and of course David still meant a great deal to me. But, darling, David has gone. Where, I don't know, but gone he has. There's only you, and what I feel for you is a far bigger, far deeper thing than I ever felt for David.'

His arm about her tightened so that it almost hurt. ' You're sure? Really sure?'

' I'm very, very sure. Far from merely tolerating you, I liked you from the morning of our first interview.'

His eyes widened. ' You had a very odd way of showing it.'

' I fought against it. Celia was always there. She was much more real than David's ghost. You drew her face in your doodlings, you carried her photograph in your pocket, you left your father's business because of her and—'

He stared at her. 'What a fearful imagination you have!'

'You mean it's not true?'

'Not a word of it. I left the oil business because I just couldn't stand the cut and thrust of big business any longer. And that wasn't Celia's face I was drawing. I always draw faces when I'm doodling. As to the photograph, I'd forgotten it was there. Celia put it into my pocket one time. She was my secretary, that was all. At a risk of sounding conceited I think she did rather want to marry me. Not because she loved me or because I'd ever given her any encouragement. It was money and position she wanted, and she considered I had it. And don't forget,' he said with a grin, 'you invited her to stay at the houseboat, not I.'

'I did it to please you, then spent every minute regretting it,' she told him. Then: 'By the way, did you know that she and Max had met each other before—'

He nodded. 'I've had a very busy week finding out things. I went to see Sheldrake and threatened to put the police on to him if he didn't tell me the truth. Then I went to see Windham and scared him half to death, and finally I got a few things out of Celia.'

'Mm. A very determined man, weren't you?'

'That was me all right, after I'd come to my senses. It's been a pretty fair conspiracy. Windham and Celia met one day in town, it seemed, and thoroughly got their heads together. She wanted to get me back to London with the hope of becoming wife of the heir to the oil company, he wanted Wingcraft. At first he had hoped to get possession simply by marrying you. He hadn't enough money to buy it himself.'

'Sounds feasible. I know he was fed up with working for his father.'

'It's true. I got that much from Celia. When he

realized there was nothing doing as far as you were concerned he promised to help Celia to try to get me so fed
up I'd leave and go back to London. Celia suspected
how I felt about you which made her all the more anxious
to drive a wedge between us. In fact, Celia promised
Max a considerable sum of money once she had my ring
on her finger. I suspect one idea was to make it appear
that you were keen on him by various means. But those
antics failed miserably. You told me you didn't particularly care for him, in any case. I believed you, but
it only confirmed worse suspicions. That you were still
in love with David's ghost.'

Julia clung to him. 'Silly! But they very nearly
succeeded in one way, didn't they? I really thought you
intended marrying Celia, especially when you said you
were going back to London, and I couldn't bear the
thought of you bringing her back to the boatyard—and
the house—after you were married. That's why I ran
away.'

He lifted her chin and looked into her eyes. 'Darling
girl, I had that house done up for you. I had every
intention of asking you to marry me one day, until—'

She silenced him by putting her lips on his. Then
after a minute or two:

'Did you find out who had monkeyed with the design
for the new yachts?'

He nodded. You remember the Sunday when the
cruiser got stuck on Breydon Water? Windham rang
Sheldrake—and by the way, he'd been paid to come and
try to sabotage the business so that I'd get fed up and
pack it in, and by bringing down the reputation of
Wingcraft, Windham hoped to get it cheaper. Anyway,
that Sunday Windham kept Bob Winters talking while
Sheldrake photographed the design. Then they got a
tracing done and altered the figures. It was easy for
Sheldrake to make the exchange without the design ever
being missed. But, sweetheart, I didn't mean what I
said that morning. I was so wretched because I thought

you wanted to get rid of me. Promise you'll never, ever run away from me again, for I just couldn't live without you.'

'Nor I without you,' she answered softly.